Fast Forms

FOR YOUTH
MINISTRY

COMPILED BY LEE SPARKS

Group Books

Loveland, Colorado

Fast Forms for Youth Ministry

Copyright © 1987 by Thom Schultz Publications, Inc.
Sixth Printing, 1993

Edited by Nancy M. Shaw
Designed by Judy Atwood
Artwork by Jan Aufdemberge, Jan Knudson
Cover design by Jean Bruns
Typography by Suzi Jensen, Peggy Mathiesen

Scripture quotations are from the Holy Bible, New International Version. Copyright © 1973, 1978, 1984 International Bible Society. Used by permission of Zondervan Bible Publishers.

Library of Congress Cataloging-in-Publication Data
Fast forms for youth ministry.

1. Church work with youth—Forms. I. Sparks, Lee.
BV4447.F37 1987   254   87-17692
ISBN 0-931529-25-5 (pbk.)

Printed in the United States of America

Contents

PART SIX: FUND RAISING

PART SEVEN: PLANNING

PART EIGHT: COMMUNICATIONS

PART NINE: RECORDS

CONTRIBUTORS

Introduction

Paper work.

The mere mention of paper work strikes dread into the minds of many youth workers. Working with young people, by nature, is a people-oriented profession. Yet *many* administrative tasks need to be done. Some of these tasks repeat themselves. *Fast Forms for Youth Ministry* will help you streamline your paper work and administrative tasks. This book's primary purpose is to help you stop "reinventing the wheel" by providing you with 70 commonly used checklists, letters, forms, job descriptions, inventories, etc., for all aspects of youth ministry:

Employment—forms for the job-related needs of youth workers, such as job descriptions, sample resume, evaluations and so on.

Parents—forms for keeping parents informed and for securing their permission for various activities.

Volunteers—forms for recruiting, training and supporting the adults who give their most precious resource: their time.

Meetings—forms for preparing and evaluating Bible studies, fellowship meetings, Sunday school sessions, etc.

Trips and Retreats—forms for planning where to go, when to go, how to go, conduct covenants, etc.

Fund Raising—forms for raising money.

Planning—forms for organizing your life goals, your time and your ministry.

Communications—forms for getting the word out, producing newsletters and posters, publicizing your events, expressing your appreciation, etc.

Records—forms for keeping information up-to-date, keeping track of kids' interests, logging expenses, etc.

We encourage you to keep your files up-to-date with the information gleaned through these forms. Remember, information is useful *only* if it is accessible and current. Whenever possible, toss out old, duplicate or unnecessary information. Store the information you gather in a way that makes most sense to you, as long as the information is easily accessible and up-to-date.

We hope you find these sample letters, checklists, inventories and other common forms helpful in your work with young people. As you streamline your paper work, you will have more valuable time to minister with young people.

Ideas for books come from many sources. We thank Dr. Merrill E. Douglass, director of the Time Management Center, whose classes at the 1987 Youth Ministry University provided the "seed" from which grew *Fast Forms for Youth Ministry*. His time management resources are among the best available.

PART ONE:

Employment

Youth Minister Resume

A resume is often your first introduction to a potential employer. A youth worker's resume needs to present a professional image of you to that employer. The sample that follows suggests one approach to designing your resume.

Always choose a format that stresses your strengths. The following format promotes the person's skills over his education and experience. You may prefer to emphasize your education or experience. If you choose to include areas of expertise, highlight two or three of your strengths and give examples of each. Include areas like administration, counseling, organization, knowledge of youth culture and so on. Include as references teenagers, parents of teenagers and pastors with whom you've worked. Most resumes need not exceed one page. Remember, a resume should introduce yourself to others, not tell your life story in detail.

Many print shops will typeset and print resumes for a minimal cost. Your resume may also be typed, but be sure you proofread for errors. A poor resume can disqualify you for a job you may be qualified to handle. Present yourself as a professional, especially on paper.

YOUTH MINISTER RESUME

(Sample)

Joseph L. Freeman
111 Cooper Drive, Apartment 23
Winston, Arizona 80594

OCCUPATIONAL OBJECTIVE

Position of youth minister in a small evangelical church

EDUCATION

- B.A.; Aurora University; Aurora, Illinois; May, 1982
  Major: Christian studies
  Cumulative grade-point average: 3.9/4.0
- M.Div.; Fuller Theological Seminary; Pasadena, California; April, 1987
  Special emphases: Youth ministry, Christian education
  Cumulative grade-point average: 3.5/4.0

AREAS OF EXPERTISE

Teaching
- Taught senior high Sunday school classes for six years
- Student-taught undergraduate-level classes on The Prophets, Introduction to Christian Studies and Effective Youth Ministry
- Served as a congregational Christian education board member in charge of junior and senior high curriculum for one year

Leadership
- Elected president of student body at Aurora University
- Performed as chairman for the Aurora United Way fund drive in 1983. Helped increase giving by 9 percent over previous year
- Coordinated summer ministry program for First United Church senior high youth group

Program Development
- Developed and implemented a program for parents and young people to work together in developing an anti-drug campaign
- Wrote an eight-week study course on the book of Colossians for senior high Sunday school students
- Developed a service program for junior high students. Involved them in painting houses, mowing lawns and performing other services for low-income communities
- Designed a youth ministry model for a local church that did not have a full-time youth minister

RELATED WORK EXPERIENCE
- Youth ministry intern; First United Church; Pasadena, California; May, 1986 to April, 1987
- Interim youth minister; Faith Church, Aurora, Illinois; May, 1982 to September, 1982
- Camp counselor; Lakeside Church Camp; Waterville, Maine; summers 1979-81

HONORS

Thomas K. Lewis Scholarship, 1984-87
Community Service Award, 1983
Vice-Presidential Leadership Scholarship, 1978-81

INTERESTS

Hiking, photography, music, sports, reading, traveling

REFERENCES

Available on request

Youth Minister Job Description

The purpose of a written job description is to give the congregation and the youth minister a clear understanding of work expectations. The job description protects the youth minister from being assigned tasks beyond his or her immediate responsibilities. The job description also gives the congregation a specific way to evaluate the work performed by the youth minister.

No job description can cover every situation or circumstance in ministry. Thus the accountability section of the job description describes the process by which ministry happens in the church. It is important to have the youth minister responsible to a congregational committee as well as to a staff or senior minister. Feedback from the youth minister's supervisor and lay committee gives the youth minister general guidelines for implementing ministry. If staff or church members ask the youth minister to do tasks far afield from this job description, the youth minister should discuss the problem with those directly involved. He or she can also refer everyone involved back to the job description and seek clarification of the ministry tasks listed.

The following definitions may help clarify this job description:

Youth council refers to adult volunteer youth workers, teachers and youth group officers or representatives.

A *youth ministry committee* is a congregational group of adults and young people who are responsible for the general policies and long-range goals of youth ministry within the congregation.

Make sure the church and the youth minister understand and agree on how Social Security will be part of the salary package. It may be understood in two ways. First, if the youth minister is self-employed, the Social Security amount would be fixed as a benefit to offset the amount of tax the youth minister is required to pay personally. Second, if the youth minister is an employee of the church, then the Social Security amount the church pays becomes an added expense to the church and should be calculated by the church as an expense associated with this position.

YOUTH MINISTER JOB DESCRIPTION

The youth minister shall be a well-trained professional, committed to Jesus Christ and to ministry with young people and their families. The youth minister shall possess the administrative skills necessary to perform his or her duties and carry out details, as well as the interpersonal, relational skills for working with kids and adults within the congregation.

Responsibilities

1. Recruit, train, encourage and support lay people in the various volunteer ministries of working with young people in our congregation.
   - Provide regular training sessions for teachers and volunteers.
   - Have regular volunteer and teacher meetings for planning and programming.
   - Work with the youth ministry committee to identify and recruit potential volunteer youth workers.
   - Help recruit volunteer youth workers.
   - Locate and use valuable resources like youth workers magazines, periodicals and curricula relevant to youth ministry.

2. Support young people and adults in planning and programming evening fellowships.
   - Work closely with the youth council. (See introduction to this form.)
   - Develop a quarterly calendar of youth programs and events.
   - Help implement plans by ordering needed materials, scheduling speakers, handling setup details for events, etc.
   - Attend evening fellowships whenever possible.

3. Provide for growth of youth groups.
   - Arrange for regular pastoral visits to active, inactive and prospective young people.
   - Develop effective publicity for youth activities through the church newsletter, school newspapers, a youth newsletter, mailings, media publicity, etc.
   - Research and schedule special events such as camps and conferences, seminars, retreats, lock-ins, trips and so on.
   - Train young people and plan for special evangelistic outreach to other teenagers in the community.
   - Locate resources to meet the needs of smaller groups in such areas as spiritual growth, Bible study, drama, clown or puppet ministry, personal and interpersonal growth, and so on.
   - Offer service opportunities throughout the year to involve young people in missions, community service, workcamping experiences, etc.

4. Work with the youth and education committees to coordinate youth ministry with the ministry of the total church.
   - Provide the committees with information about quality resources for curriculum materials.
   - Offer ideas and personal input about future goals for the church's ministry with young people.

5. Build relationships with the parents of young people in the youth groups.
   - Visit young people in their homes.
   - Provide resource seminars for parents based on their needs (see Parent Survey page 23 and Parent Information Form page 25).
   - Call on young people and parents in pastoral-need situations such as sickness, hospitalization, crisis intervention, death and other situations in which teenagers may need help or support.
   - Meet with parents at least three times a year to communicate about the youth calendar, volunteer needs, parental concerns, etc.

6. Work with adult volunteers and other members of the congregation to make youth ministry an effective effort.

7. Work as a professional with the other ministry staff to provide for the pastoral needs of the congregation.

8. Attend workshops and personal growth conferences to stay informed on new and effective ways to implement youth ministry.

9. Lead the congregation members as they establish long-range goals and short-term objectives for an ongoing youth ministry in the life of the church.

Accountability

1. The senior minister and the youth ministry committee will supervise the work of the youth minister.

2. The youth minister will provide a written report to summarize his or her work for the past month.

3. The youth minister will communicate the plans and activities of the young people to the professional staff, the church planning council and youth ministry committee.

4. The youth minister will be evaluated annually by the church's professional staff, the youth ministry committee and the youth council. A written report will be provided and explained.

5. Should the youth minister feel mistreated by any staff, church member or committee in the congregation, the youth minister may discuss any grievances confidentially within the pastoral relations committee.

6. The congregation or youth minister may dissolve this agreement by giving 30 days notice.

Compensation

1. Basic package (annually)
Base salary $ _____
Housing allowance $ _____
Utilities allowance $ _____

2. Benefits (annually)
Retirement $ _____
Car allowance $ _____
Health insurance $ _____
Social Security allowance $ _____
Books and subscriptions $ _____
Continuing education $ _____

3. Vacation time: _____ weeks per year.

4. Other:

This job description is entered into in good faith through a commitment to serve Jesus Christ and his church on this day _____ of _____ in the year _____.
(Month)

_____   _____
            Youth minister   Congregational official

Letter of Call for Youth Minister

A letter of call generally affirms a candidate as the person the church wishes to have fill the position of youth minister. Two job descriptions (see page 11) signed by an official of the congregation should accompany this letter.

If the candidate wants to accept this position, he or she should promptly sign both copies of the job description, keep one for his or her files and return the other to the church.

LETTER OF CALL FOR YOUTH MINISTER

Dear _____,

On _____, _____
       (Date)   (Name of church or whatever official group)
voted to call you as youth minister.

Enclosed are two copies of the proposed job description, including the
compensation package. Please sign both copies. Keep one for yourself
and return one to us before _____. The signed job
                                 (Date)
description will be our contract agreement, defining the terms and
conditions of your call as our youth minister.

Our congregation also agrees to provide for the costs of your moving to
our community in an amount not to exceed $_____.
Additional moving or housing costs need to be negotiated with

_____.
  (Name)

We believe God has brought us together for his mutual ministry with the
young people in our congregation. We will be praying for you as you
faithfully consider this call.

Please contact us should you have any questions.

In God's service,

_____
(Name)

_____
(Position)

Youth Minister Evaluations

The youth minister needs objective input from both adults and young people through periodic evaluations. Such evaluations might be prepared by teenagers and adults at least twice a year. Pass out current copies of the youth minister's job description, and ask the following people to complete an evaluation: professional ministry staff, clerical support staff, youth ministry committee members, church leaders and the members of the youth council, including volunteers, teachers and youth group officers or representatives.

The youth minister will profit by reading the evaluations and discussing them with other ministerial staff and the youth ministry committee.

YOUTH MINISTER EVALUATION
(By young person)

What I like best about _____
(Name of youth minister)

What I don't like about him/her:

What I would like to see our youth group do *less* of in the future:

What I would like to see our youth group do *more* of in the future:

Evaluation completed by _____

Note: It is not necessary to sign this form.

YOUTH MINISTER EVALUATION

(By adult)

1. Read the accompanying copy of the youth minister's job description.

2. Be as open and candid about your observations as possible. It is not necessary for you to sign your name to this evaluation.

3. On a scale from 1 to 10, with 1 being "Awful" and 10 being "Outstanding," how do you feel our youth minister rates in the following areas? Respond only to those factors of which you have knowledge. Please write the number for your response in the appropriate column. If you have gained your knowledge as a bystander or a distant observer, write your response under the "General Impression" column. If you have worked closely with the youth minister in a particular area, write your response in the "Personal Knowledge" column.

A. Job Performance: (How well the youth minister carries out the duties of the current position)

	General Impression	Personal knowledge
1. Attitude: enthusiastic, constructive, optimistic, loyal; good orientation to church, position and associates.	_____	_____
2. Initiative: self-starting; prompt to take hold of a problem; sees and acts on new opportunities.	_____	_____
3. Motivation: has well-planned goals; willingly assumes greater responsibilities; realistically ambitious.	_____	_____
4. Verbal facility: articulate; communicative; generally understood by people at all levels.	_____	_____
5. Technical knowledge: knowledge of functional skills needed to carry out position requirements.	_____	_____
6. Acuteness: mentally alert; understands unusual situations and circumstances quickly.	_____	_____
7. Sociability: makes friends easily; works "comfortably" with others; has sincere interest in people.	_____	_____
8. Dependability: meets schedules and deadlines; adheres to instructions and policy.	_____	_____
9. Self-control: calm and poised under pressure.	_____	_____
10. Sensitivity: has a "feel" for people, recognizes their problems; quick to pick up "the way the wind is blowing"; considerate of others.	_____	_____
11. Leadership: receives loyalty and cooperation from others; manages and motivates others to full effectiveness.	_____	_____
12. Objectivity: has an open mind; keeps emotional or personal interests from influencing decisions.	_____	_____
13. Accomplishment: effective use of time.	_____	_____
14. Acceptance: gains confidence of others; gains respect.	_____	_____
15. Flexibility: adaptable; adjusts rapidly to changing conditions; copes with the unexpected.	_____	_____
16. Quality: accurate and thorough, high standards.	_____	_____
17. Self-confidence: assured, bears inner security.	_____	_____
18. Human relationship skills: ability to motivate people, helps people work together as a team.	_____	_____

(over)

19. **Drive:** works with energy, not easily discouraged; basic urge to get things done.   _____   _____
20. **Intellectual ability:** ability to solve problems, adapt to new situations, analyze and make judgments.   _____   _____
21. **Administration:** organizes work for self and others; delegates responsibilities and follows up on assignments.   _____   _____
22. **Frugal:** effective at deriving the greatest possible benefit from limited financial resources.   _____   _____
23. **Analysis and judgment:** critical observer; breaks problem into components, weighs and relates; arrives at sound conclusions.   _____   _____
24. **Creativity:** original ideas; an inquiring mind; fresh approach to problems.   _____   _____
25. **Capacity:** mental depth and breadth; reservoir of mental ability.   _____   _____
26. **Vision:** has foresight; sees new opportunities and appreciates them but is not bound by tradition and custom.   _____   _____
27. **Professionalism:** ethical, mature; displays tact and diplomacy.   _____   _____

B. Personal Performance:

1. Demonstrates sincerity in dealing with people.   _____   _____
2. Has a sense of humor appropriate to the occasion.   _____   _____
3. Is resilient; can handle setbacks maturely and learn from mistakes.   _____   _____
4. Has rapport with church staff.   _____   _____
5. Works well within his/her range of authority.   _____   _____
6. Represents the church effectively within the community.   _____   _____
7. Represents accurately the interests, concerns and basic tenets of our denomination.   _____   _____
8. Likes to be around teenagers.   _____   _____

C. Summary:

1. Please list what you believe are the youth minister's three main strengths in his/her present position.

2. Please list three areas in which you believe the youth minister could make improvements in his/her present position.

3. Feel free to give comments (affirmations and concerns) on any area mentioned above.

Employee Evaluation

An evaluation form needs to be simple and easily understood by both the supervisor and the employee. An evaluation is usually completed after an initial probation period on the job and annually thereafter.

If the employee being evaluated is a clerical person, specific skills such as typing, answering the phone and other tasks may need evaluation. A clerical person is usually a vital link in a church's youth ministry program. For example, a negative or hostile secretary can severely hamper a youth minister's effectiveness, but an excellent secretary can significantly enhance any program's efficiency.

If the youth minister shares clerical support with other staff ministers, the youth minister should be one of those involved both in hiring and dismissing that person.

Both the employee and the supervisor should fill out a copy of this form. Then they meet to compare the employee's self-evaluation to the supervisor's evaluation of the employee.

EMPLOYEE EVALUATION

Employee name: _____

Position: _____

Date of evaluation: _____

Rate the employee according to these standards:

    1-Poor   2-Average   3-Above average   4-Excellent

_____ Dependability

_____ Cooperation

_____ Motivation

_____ Initiative

_____ Relationships with other employees

_____ Relationships with other church members

_____ Relationships with youth

_____ Organization of work

_____ Completion of tasks on time

_____ Neat and high quality work

_____ Professional, mature attitude

_____ Sense of humor

_____ Christian traits in all relationships

_____ Technical skills such as _____

The strengths consistently demonstrated by this employee:

This employee needs to improve:

General comments:

Supervisor's signature: _____

PART TWO:

Parents

Parent Survey

Parents can definitely influence their teenager's decision about how involved he or she will be in the youth program. That's one reason why input from parents is invaluable. This parent survey asks for feedback from parents and determines the level of involvement in which they might be interested. Since youth programs vary considerably, use the following instrument as a guide for developing your own survey.

Two-way communication is important for successfully involving parents in your program. Share the results of this survey with both the parents and their young people. Use the results to open the doors of communication between parents, teenagers and the church. Provide opportunities to answer the questions and needs of parents. Involve those parents who indicate a desire to help or serve. Offer occasional programs that involve parents and teenagers in mutual experiences. When you ask parents for their input and then offer opportunities for them to get involved, they are much more inclined to support your efforts and their teenager's involvement.

PARENT SURVEY

The youth group at our church is YOUR youth group, too. We are interested in your input and assistance to help make this the best youth group possible. Please take a few moments to complete the following survey.

How Can We Help You?

How can the youth program serve the needs of your young people?

How can the youth group leader(s) help support your needs as a parent?

What expectations do you have of the youth leader(s) and the youth program?

What suggestions do you have?

What days and times for youth meetings and events are most convenient for your family?

How Can You Help Us?

Would you be willing to help in one or more of the following areas? (Indicate "yes" or "no" and best day or time below):

Provide refreshments for a meeting?	_____	Best Time _____
Host a meeting at your home?	_____	Best Time _____
Be a driver for an event?	_____	Best Time _____
If yes, are you licensed to drive the church van or bus?	_____	Best Time _____
Be a special speaker for a meeting?	_____	Best Time _____
Assist in planning a meeting?	_____	Best Time _____
Be a volunteer for a one-time event?	_____	Best Time _____
Serve on the youth advisory council? (One meeting a month)	_____	Best Time _____

Other ways you would like to help _____

_____

_____

What questions or concerns do *you* have about the youth program?
(Please use the back of this page.)

Parent Information Form and Commitment Letter

Seek as much information as possible about parents or guardians. This knowledge will help you meet the needs of your young people through relationships and programming.

Two settings offer excellent opportunities for obtaining this information: a parents meeting early each fall or individual interviews with parents during a visit to their home. Mailing this form to parents and expecting them to return it is the least effective way to obtain this information, since response would be minimal.

Assure parents that you will keep the Parent Information Form confidential. That way adults won't feel that other church programs will recruit them based on the information in this form.

Update your information forms annually. If possible, attach a picture of the family to your form. Fill out forms on non-member families. These are excellent resources for outreach and evangelism.

The Parent Commitment Letter should be signed at the end of each parents meeting or after a home visit by the youth pastor. Listen to parents who hesitate or refuse to sign this letter. They may have deep concerns or needs that warrant pastoral care.

PARENT INFORMATION FORM

Young person's name (Last name first) _____

Mother's name _____

Father's name_____

Guardian (If applicable) _____

Other siblings and ages _____

_____

Street address _____

City _____ Zip _____ Phone _____

Mother's occupation _____

Place of employment _____ Phone _____

Father's occupation _____

Place of employment _____ Phone _____

Mother's hobbies, interests, sports _____

_____

Father's hobbies, interests, sports_____

_____

Marital status _____ Married _____ Separated _____ Divorced _____ Widowed

Address and phone of non-custodial parent (If applicable) _____

_____

Comments

(over)

Use the initials of each parent to mark areas of interest or to indicate where he or she is willing to volunteer:

_____ Snack supper

_____ Provide transportation

_____ Youth librarian

_____ Sponsor at youth events

_____ Teach

_____ Visit families with prospective new youth

_____ Work with evening fellowship

_____ Work with youth choir

_____ Youth council

_____ Help with youth fund raising

_____ Host meetings

_____ Assist young people with service projects

List any special skills or talents (such as drama, clown ministry, puppets, photography, carpentry, cooking, mechanics and so on) that either parent might be willing to share with the young people:

What do the parents expect the church's youth ministry to do for their children?

What do the parents need from the church's youth ministry?

PARENT COMMITMENT LETTER

Dear Parent(s) or Guardian(s):

Today _____ you have attended the parents meeting or have visited
(Date)
with the youth minister about the following items:

- the youth calendar for _____ through _____;
(Month)   (Month)
- the volunteer tasks that are needed from parents during this period of time;
- the code of conduct for young people in our youth programs;
- program materials and study topics for evening fellowships in our church;
- curriculum taught in our Sunday school;
- plans for youth lock-ins, trips and retreats, including costs and details; plus
- the long-range goals and objectives for our youth ministry program.

If you approve of these plans and programs, please indicate your support by doing the following:

- commit yourself to encourage your young person to participate;
- bring your young person to youth activities;
- volunteer for tasks you are willing to undertake;
- affirm the importance of youth ministry to other adults within the
congregation;
- support funding for youth ministry by giving to the church budget; and
- pray for all our young people, plus the volunteers and church staff who
work with them.

If you are willing to make this commitment, please sign this letter on the lines
below.

_____
Mother (or Guardian)

_____
Father (or Guardian)

Liability Release and Parental Consent Forms

Today's laws and practices have made many churches apprehensive about trips or activities that put their young people at risk. Most parents understand the risks involved and are willing to relieve the church and its employees of any liability for their young people. They realize their teenagers have minds of their own. But they do expect the church to help when an emergency occurs.

These two forms provide ways for both the church and parents to recognize and accept their own responsibilities. The Liability Release Form can be used as a legal document to release the church from all liability claims. It also contains enough information to be used as a medical authorization and a parental consent form.

The Parental Consent Form authorizes adults within the organization to consent to medical procedures suggested for their child in case of emergency. It clarifies parental financial responsibility for any treatment needed. This form also provides a permission statement for adult volunteers to decide in which vehicle a child will ride.

LIABILITY RELEASE FORM

Release of All Claims

In consideration for being accepted by _____ for participation in

(Church name)

_____, we (I), being 21 years of age or older, do for

(Name of trip or activity)

our selves (myself) (and for and on behalf of my child-participant if said child is not 21 years of age or

older) do hereby release, forever discharge and agree to hold harmless _____

(Church name)

and the directors thereof from any and all liability, claims or demands for personal injury, sickness or death, as well as property damage and expenses, of any nature whatsoever which may be incurred by the undersigned and the child-participant that occur while said child is participating in the above-described trip or activity.

Furthermore, we (I) [and on behalf of our (my) child-participant if under the age of 21 years] hereby assume all risk of personal injury, sickness, death, damage and expense as a result of participation in recreation and work activities involved therein.

Further, authorization and permission is hereby given to said church to furnish any necessary transportation, food and lodging for this participant.

The undersigned further hereby agree to hold harmless and indemnify said church, its directors, employees and agents, for any liability sustained by said church as the result of the negligent, willful or intentional acts of said participant, including expenses incurred attendant thereto.

(If the participant has not attained the age of 21 years):

We (I) are the parent(s) or legal guardian(s) of this participant, and hereby grant our (my) permission for him (her) to participate fully in said trip, and hereby give our (my) permission to take said participant to a doctor or hospital and hereby authorize medical treatment, including but not in limitation to emergency surgery or medical treatment, and assume the responsibility of all medical bills, if any.

Further, should it be necessary for the participant to return home due to medical reasons, disciplinary action or otherwise, we (I) hereby assume all transportation costs.

_____

(Type or print name of participant)

_____

[Parent(s) telephone]

_____

(Pastor's telephone)

Hospital insurance ☐Yes ☐No

Insurance company

_____

Policy number_____

Physician _____

Physician's phone _____

Emergency phone numbers_____

_____

(Only participant need sign if 21 years of age or older. If under 21, *both* parents must sign unless parents are separated or divorced in which case the custodial parent must sign.)

_____

Father   Date

_____

Mother   Date

_____

Legal guardian   Date

_____

Participant, if age 21   Date

Trip Participant Only

I have read the foregoing and understand the rules of conduct for participants and will abide by them as well as the directions of the leadership of the trip.

_____

Participant

PARENTAL CONSENT FORM

Name_____ Age _____ Birth date _____

Address_____ Phone (_____)_____

City_____ State_____ Zip code_____

School _____ Grade in or just completed _____

Parent(s) business phones _____

_____

To whom it may concern:

The undersigned does hereby give permission for our (my) child, _____

_____, to attend and participate in
                (Name of child)

activities sponsored by _____ on _____.
                              Church   (Date)

We (I) authorize an adult, in whose care the minor has been entrusted, to consent to any X-ray examination, anesthetic, medical, surgical or dental diagnosis or treatment, and hospital care, to be rendered to the minor under the general or special supervision and on the advice of any physician or dentist licensed under the provisions of the Medical Practice Act on the medical staff of a licensed hospital, whether such diagnosis or treatment is rendered at the office of said physician or at said hospital.

The undersigned shall be liable and agree(s) to pay all costs and expenses incurred in connection with such medical and dental services rendered to the aforementioned child pursuant to this authorization.

Should it be necessary for our (my) child to return home due to medical reasons or otherwise, the undersigned shall assume all transportation costs.

The undersigned does also hereby give permission for our (my) child to ride in any vehicle designated by the adult in whose care the minor has been entrusted while attending and participating in activities sponsored by _____.
                                                                                    (Church)

Hospital insurance   Yes ☐   No ☐

Insurance company_____

Policy number _____

Emergency phone numbers _____

_____

_____
Participant   Date

_____
Father   Date

_____
Mother   Date

_____
Legal guardian   Date

On the reverse side of this page, please list any allergies or special medical problems your child may have. Thank you.

Overnight Permission Letter

Overnight activities at church can be great fun. They present few transportation hassles, and the price is usually right. Leaders have less busywork with rides and money and more time to focus on other matters. No matter how much time it takes, remember to add a parent permission form to your preparations.

It seems like a lot of busy work. Right? Wrong! This form may save you from hassles with irate parents and even from legal troubles. A permission letter protects the youth worker and the church if kids sneak off, don't show up or present discipline problems.

When combined with a medical release, this form can save precious time in a medical emergency. Combined with a legal release, this form can protect the church from lawsuits if any kind of injury occurs on church property during the event.

Remember, the best way to set rules is as a *group*. Young people (and adults) tend to abide by rules they themselves establish.

OVERNIGHT PERMISSION LETTER

I give permission for _____ to attend the church
                              (Name of child)

overnight on _____ at _____.
                    (Date)   (Place)

I understand this event begins at _____ and ends at
                                          (Time)

_____ .
        (Time)

I also understand that these are the basic rules for this overnight event, which have been agreed upon by the youth group and volunteers:

1.

2.

3.

4.

5.

If my young person or his or her guest has problems with these ground rules, I agree to pick him or her up immediately.

Sincerely,

Parent/guardian: _____

PART THREE:

Volunteers

Volunteer Youth Worker
Job Description

When writing a job description for a volunteer youth worker, be as specific as possible. Let people know what you expect from someone who assumes this position. Define how long you expect a person to serve. Tell people specifically what *you* can and will do for them. Once someone has volunteered, sit down with that person and fully explain his or her responsibilities. Be honest; tell the person exactly what is expected of him or her. Give him or her the names of other volunteer youth workers so he or she can find out more about the job from them.

VOLUNTEER YOUTH WORKER JOB DESCRIPTION

By saying "yes" to volunteering for youth ministry in our congregation, you have stated your belief that young people are important to the life of the church. As a volunteer, you will give a significant amount of your time and talents. Our youth ministry team recognizes your commitment and pledges to support your efforts. Following are our expectations of you and your expectation of us.

As a volunteer youth worker, you are expected to:

- Work with a team of adults and young people in planning and implementing the youth ministry program of the congregation.
- Know and coordinate the long-range youth ministry purposes and goals with those of the church.
- Be present at youth meetings whenever possible.
- Attend youth council meetings.
- Be prepared for all assigned tasks to which you agree.
- Be willing to call on young people with the phone or through home visits to the extent that time permits.
- Let other members of the team know when you cannot attend a youth meeting or event.
- Be a Christian example in conduct and speech for the young people.
- Serve for a period of one year with willingness to serve a second year, if invited by the youth ministry committee.
- Serve no longer than three years in succession.
- Give at least one month's notice of resignation, unless due to an emergency.
- Pray for other members of the team and youth group members.

The congregation, youth ministry committee and youth minister agree to:

- Keep you well-informed of all youth group plans and programs.
- Provide you with training to be a youth worker.
- Provide resources such as books, materials and films, and share their personal experience in ministry to help you do your job.
- Pray for you.
- Provide babysitting for your preschool and elementary children during youth meetings and other events, either at church or in your home.
- Pay your expenses on youth events and trips.
- Listen to your needs and concerns.

Other agreements, expectations, etc.:

Signature of youth minister: _____

Signature of volunteer youth worker: _____

Date: _____

Youth Council Job Description

Exactly what does a member of the youth council do? Here is a sample job description for a youth council or youth governing board member. Use this guideline to develop the job description for your own youth council members. Define expectations, and list specific responsibilities within the description.

Discuss this job description with past and present youth council members. Their feedback will help you formulate an accurate picture of the position so you can talk with potential members. Remember, the youth council is usually a steering committee, not a "do-it-all" group of workaholics. Its primary mission is to direct and support the policies for youth ministry.

Many churches have some kind of governing board composed of adults (and sometimes also youth). Some call this policy-making group the "youth committee," "youth board," "youth council," "youth task force," etc. For our purposes, we'll refer to it as youth council.

YOUTH COUNCIL JOB DESCRIPTION

(Sample)

The head of the youth council is the youth minister.

A member of the youth council must:

- have a willingness to serve;
- desire to help the youth program succeed;
- have excitement about the possibilities;
- have a sense of adventure and creativity; and
- understand the youth culture.

General Responsibilities

A youth council member will:

- be a youth ministry advocate within the congregation;
- listen to the needs of the young people, pastors and other church members;
- assist in determining youth ministry policies (ages or grade levels when young people may enter the various programs, travel rules, health regulations, etc.);
- act as a sounding board for problems and disagreements within the youth program or in relation to the rest of the congregation; and
- create opportunities for young people to involve themselves in other areas of church life.

Other Responsibilities

A youth council member will:

- attend one meeting a month;
- serve to fulfill the goals of the youth council;
- listen to the needs of the youth program;
- go through proper church channels to implement new procedures, policies or programs;
- help evaluate the success of specific programs and suggest changes when needed; and
- serve on the council for a term of two years.

Volunteer Profile

Volunteer youth workers can come from all segments of your congregation—the young adult who remembers how special his or her youth group was; young parents who want to make sure youth programming will remain a priority for their children; parents with children in the program; and older or retired individuals who just like to be around kids. All of these individuals can offer different resources for your program.

To say that all it takes to be a good youth worker is a desire to work with young people is partially true. Be wary of individuals and personalities whose philosophy of youth work is not conducive to your particular ministry.

This profile provides a lot of factual information plus some insight into an individual's personality. Most people can be plugged into the program in some creative way.

VOLUNTEER PROFILE

Name _____ Phone number _____

Address _____ Birth date _____

City _____ State _____ Zip _____

Marital status: _____ Single _____ Married _____ Separated _____ Divorced _____ Widowed

Name of spouse (if applicable) _____

Names and ages of children (if applicable) _____

_____

_____

Occupation _____

Place of employment _____ Phone _____

Hobbies, interests, sports_____

_____

Schedule of ongoing family/personal activities—On the calendar below, circle and note times you would be available to work in the youth program. If you can work on Wednesday mornings from 9 to 11:30 a.m., write those times on the calendar and circle that block of time.

	Sun.	Mon.	Tue.	Wed.	Thu.	Fri.	Sat.
Morning							
Afternoon							
Evening							

How do you desire to work in the youth program? Check the areas that *most* interest you.

_____ Teach Sunday school

_____ Teach Bible study

_____ Work with evening fellowship

_____ Typing, filing, other clerical help

_____ Furnish transportation

_____ Chaperon at youth events

_____ Youth ministry council

_____ Help with fund raising

_____ Review books, magazine articles, tapes, records

_____ Visit teenagers in hospital

_____ Tutor teenagers who need help

_____ Assist with service projects

_____ Lead a parents' support group

_____ Host meetings

_____ Drive church vehicles

Other: _____

Volunteer Time, Talent and Interest Form

What would we do without volunteers for our youth groups? These special people offer all kinds of energy and talent for our programs. But how many times have you stumbled across some hidden interest or talent in a youth volunteer just when he or she was ready to retire?

The Volunteer Time, Talent and Interest Form offers a quick and easy way to identify the gifts these special people possess. It may also be used in the general congregation to identify areas of need within your youth group and may encourage individuals to offer their skills and services as volunteers for various activities.

So many times we overlook the older members of our churches when it comes time to look for help with the youth group. Examine the needs of your group; there are many ways everyone can help. By involving the older members of your congregation, you will establish a natural means of communication between generations and allow each group to serve the needs of the other.

VOLUNTEER TIME, TALENT AND INTEREST FORM

"How Can I Help?"

The youth program in our church needs your help. Please check those areas below where you would be willing and able to serve. Thank you!

Advertising/Publicity
_____ Prepare mailings
_____ Prepare bulletin boards
_____ Prepare posters
_____ Prepare newsletters

Education
_____ Lead Bible study
_____ Teach a class (church membership, confirmation, Sunday school, etc.)
_____ Plan program (check out missions projects, set up parent/teenager activities)

Activities
_____ Weekly meetings
_____ Retreats (junior high, high school)
_____ Lock-in
_____ Ski trip
_____ Fund raisers
_____ Service projects
_____ Workcamp
_____ Mission trip
_____ Cantata

Audio-Visual
_____ Run machines
_____ Teach how to use equipment
_____ Use equipment to create programs
_____ Sound system
_____ Slide projector
_____ Opaque projector
_____ Video camera
_____ Take pictures

Worship/Celebration
_____ Drama (direct; write; design sets or costumes; help with makeup; help with special events like the Christmas program or the Easter Sunrise service.)
_____ Clown ministry
_____ Puppet ministry
_____ Prepare banners

Music
_____ Choir (sing, direct, etc.)
_____ Play an instrument (piano, guitar, etc.)
_____ Accompany others
_____ Hand bells (play, teach, direct)

Service
_____ Visit members (inactive, new, hospital, homebound)
_____ Homework hot line (subjects, grade levels)
_____ Drive a car
_____ Drive a bus
_____ Teach how-to skills for (____ ____)
_____ Library (checkout/in, review books)
_____ Phone (call for activities, polls, etc.)
_____ Share your hobby
_____ Host activity at your home
_____ Teach time management
_____ Talent search (help others identify their skills)
_____ Kitchen help (serve, cleanup)
_____ Prepare food
_____ Provide refreshments
_____ Coach a sports team (softball, baseball, soccer, basketball, tennis, etc.)
_____ Listen to people

Letter of Call for Volunteer Youth Worker

How do you successfully recruit adult volunteers? Do you just ask a member of your church to help out, sounding almost apologetic as you ask?

Using a formal letter of call often impresses the potential youth volunteer. It emphasizes the importance of the position and identifies some of the expectations.

A good letter of call identifies the potential responsibilities of the youth volunteer. It is not a job description, but an overview of responsibilities. State the length of the term in the letter (one year, two years, etc.), and ask for a reply by a certain date. Send the letter after you've interviewed the potential volunteer youth worker and had time to discuss his or her gifts with your other leaders.

The letter of call should come from the youth governing board, youth council, youth minister or other appropriate authority within your youth program. Make prayerful decisions on whom to call and allow him or her time to consider prayerfully that call to serve.

LETTER OF CALL FOR VOLUNTEER YOUTH WORKER

(Sample)

April 2, 1990

Martha L. James
238 S. Randall
Aurora, IL 60505

Dear Martha,

You have some very special gifts. The members of the Youth Governing Board of First United Church would like you to consider sharing those gifts with the youth fellowship.

We would like you to consider a call to be one of our youth sponsors. A youth sponsor is an important member of the youth ministry team. Youth sponsors help to plan, organize and implement programs for the senior high youth of our church.

Although the responsibilities of a sponsor vary from program to program, the importance of the position cannot be emphasized enough. Since youth sponsors are role models for the young people of our church, being a role model takes commitment from you. We ask that you commit to a term of two years as a youth sponsor so that we can maintain a sense of consistency and continuity in the youth program.

As youth sponsors, you will get to know the teenagers of our church intimately. You will share in their successes and comfort them in times of need. You will find the role sometimes exhilarating, sometimes exhausting, but always rewarding. The Youth Governing Board, the youth ministry team and I will support you in your ministry.

We would like to count on you. Please prayerfully consider joining our team. Let us know your decision by April 20. Please call me if you have any questions.

In His service,

Stephen

Stephen Paulson, Chairman
Youth Governing Board
555-2367

Whom to Contact

Everyone knows what it is like to do something for the first time. You feel awkward and clumsy, and need support from those who have done the job before.

Whether you are a volunteer or a professional youth worker, you need to know whom to contact when questions come up. One person cannot—and should not—provide all the answers. The following form lists whom to contact for information when you need it. Insert your own information in the blank spaces provided. Update the list of people and phone numbers at least once a year.

WHOM TO CONTACT

Items:	Person:	Phone number:
Secretarial supplies	_____	_____
Janitorial supplies	_____	_____
Audio-visual supplies	_____	_____
Communion supplies	_____	_____
Drama supplies	_____	_____
Youth supplies	_____	_____

Information:

All-church calendar	_____	_____
Youth calendar	_____	_____
Insurance	_____	_____
Worship	_____	_____
Use of building/keys	_____	_____
Computer questions	_____	_____

Organization heads:

Youth council	_____	_____
Women's organizations	_____	_____
Men's organizations	_____	_____
Christian education committee	_____	_____
Church membership/ confirmation instruction	_____	_____
Budget committee	_____	_____

Order of authority (Whom do I talk to first?):

Youth minister	_____	_____
Associate minister	_____	_____
Senior minister	_____	_____
Board president	_____	_____
Trustee	_____	_____

Volunteer Evaluations

O ngoing feedback from volunteer youth workers is very important for a successful youth ministry. Volunteer evaluations help you stay on track with your programming and training.

At least once a quarter, ask each volunteer to complete an evaluation form, then get together and discuss his or her thoughts, feelings and experiences. Note any suggestions for improvement in programming, staff development, etc.

Quarterly evaluations show trends in the volunteer over the course of his or her term. These evaluations show you whether or not to ask that person back for another term. They also let you know how to support and train volunteers. Keep these evaluations for your own information. If you plan to ask the volunteer to serve again, offer to go over your evaluations with him or her in order to affirm the term's work and to challenge the volunteer to grow in the future.

VOLUNTEER EVALUATION

(By volunteer)

Name_____

On each continuum place a mark that is closest to how you feel about that statement. Respond to all questions.

1. My youth ministry responsibilities have been clearly defined.

●_____●
Agree   Disagree
Explain:

2. I have received adequate training.

●_____●
Agree   Disagree
Explain:

3. I have followed through with all assignments.

●_____●
Agree   Disagree
Explain:

4. I have received adequate help when I needed it.

●_____●
Agree   Disagree
Explain:

5. I have asked for help when I needed it.

●_____●
Agree   Disagree
Explain:

6. The youth minister has supported me.

●_____●
Agree   Disagree
Explain:

7. Fellow volunteers have supported me.

●_____●
Agree   Disagree
Explain:

(over)

8. The youth program is meeting the kids' needs.

●————————————————————————————————————●
Agree   Disagree
Explain:

9. We're effectively reaching out to new kids.

●————————————————————————————————————●
Agree   Disagree
Explain:

10. We're effectively reaching out to needy people.

●————————————————————————————————————●
Agree   Disagree
Explain:

11. Our facilities are adequate.

●————————————————————————————————————●
Agree   Disagree
Explain:

12. Rate the following retreats, Bible studies, meetings, special events, trips and other activities on a scale of 1 to 5 (1 = low; 5 = high).

Retreats
1   2   3   4   5
Ideas for other retreats:

Special events
1   2   3   4   5
Ideas for other special events:

Bible studies
1   2   3   4   5
Ideas for other Bible studies:

Trips
1   2   3   4   5
Ideas for other trips:

Meetings
1   2   3   4   5
Topics that were successes:

Ideas for other meetings:

Other activities
1   2   3   4   5
Ideas for other activities:

13. Things I like most about our youth ministry:

14. Things that can be improved:

15. Suggestions for future volunteers:

VOLUNTEER EVALUATION

(By leader)

Name of volunteer _____

On each continuum, place a mark that is closest to how you feel about that statement. Respond to all statements.

1. Volunteer followed all assigned responsibilities.

● _____ ●
Agree   Disagree
Explain:

2. Volunteer attended all training sessions.

● _____ ●
Agree   Disagree
Explain:

3. Volunteer asked for help when he or she needed it.

● _____ ●
Agree   Disagree
Explain:

4. I gave appropriate support to volunteer.

● _____ ●
Agree   Disagree
Explain:

5. Volunteer was liked and respected by fellow volunteers.

● _____ ●
Agree   Disagree
Explain:

6. The kids liked and respected volunteer.

● _____ ●
Agree   Disagree
Explain:

7. Volunteer showed a caring attitude toward kids and others.

● _____ ●
Agree   Disagree
Explain:

(over)

8. Volunteer was always dependable.

●_____●

Agree   Disagree

Explain:

9. Volunteer regularly gave positive, helpful suggestions.

●_____●

Agree   Disagree

Explain:

10. Good qualities of this volunteer (organization, motivation, skills, etc.):

11. Ways this volunteer can improve:

12. Other comments:

PART FOUR:

Meetings

Meeting Checklist

Many youth group leaders do much more than lead youth groups. With all of these responsibilities, it's easy to forget important details.

You may not need all of the items listed on the checklist for each of your meetings since they may vary. Many meetings, however, use a lot of the same ingredients including refreshments, name tags, supplies for games, paper, pencils and Bibles.

Use the checklist when you plan each meeting. Adapt it by circling the items you'll need or adding unique items that aren't listed. As soon as you gather the supplies, check them off.

MEETING CHECKLIST

Name of meeting: _____

Topic or theme: _____

Date: _____

Time: _____

Location: _____

_____ Bibles

_____ Paper

_____ Pencils

_____ Records and record player/tapes and tape player

_____ Extension cord

_____ Overhead projector

_____ Film and projector

_____ Outlet adapters

_____ Copies of materials for participants (List the materials)

_____

_____

_____

_____

_____ Name tags

_____ Supplies for games

_____ Refreshments

_____ Masking tape

_____ Chalkboard, chalk and eraser/newsprint and markers

_____ Other: _____

_____

_____

Meeting Planning Guide

Use this form to plan an evening fellowship meeting, a lock-in or some other special event or activity. Every gathering needs a purpose. It must be clearly stated and understood by both leaders and participants. For example, you might say: "The purpose of this meeting is to talk about friends. We will look at what the Bible teaches about friends, how a Christian chooses friends, and how to relate to friends."

Not every meeting or event will need each activity listed on the form.

Write materials or locate books that explain the activities you want to use. Have these resources available for your leader(s). Gather all materials you will need for the program like pencils, Bibles, construction paper, markers and so on. Finally, list step-by-step directions implementing the activity. Give special instructions under the comments section.

Carefully compare each activity you plan with your stated purpose. If it's unclear how an activity directly relates to the stated purpose, revise or delete the activity.

Remember to thank people. Affirmation encourages both young people and adults to become more active in your youth ministry program.

MEETING PLANNING GUIDE

Meeting/event: _____

Date: _____ Time: _____

Location: _____

Purpose: _____

_____

Transportation needs: _____

Publicity needs: _____

Costs: _____

Primary contact person: _____ Phone: _____

Activity	Leader(s)	Time allotted
Crowdbreakers/name tags	_____	_____

Describe resources, materials and process: _____

_____

_____

Affirmation exercises	_____	_____

Describe resources, materials and process: _____

_____

_____

Worship/singing	_____	_____

Describe resources, materials and process: _____

_____

_____

Learning	_____	_____

Describe resources, materials and process: _____

_____

_____

Games	_____	_____

Describe resources, materials and process: _____

_____

_____

(over)

Activity	Leader(s)	Time allotted

Closing
Describe resources, materials and process: _____
_____
_____

Refreshments/snacks
Describe resources, materials and process: _____
_____
_____

Cleanup

Comments _____
_____
_____
_____

Adult volunteers: _____   _____
_____   _____
_____   _____
_____   _____

Guests: _____   _____
_____   _____
_____   _____

Write thank-you notes to: _____   _____
_____   _____
_____   _____

Planning an Event

Have you ever wondered how everything will come together as you plan an event with your youth group? This form is designed to help you put all your plans in perspective.

The primary function of this form is to record specific responsibilities for all people involved in planning an event. The three main categories identified on the form are program, food and publicity. Since different kinds of events may involve other coordinators, blank coordinator sections have been provided. For example, a dinner theatre production may require a lighting-and-sound coordinator, a ticket sales coordinator and a set design coordinator. Or an evening worship program may need a music coordinator. The key to using this form successfully is to specify all coordinators' responsibilities and objectives.

Include a deadline or target date with any objective. Write that date under the correct coordinator. After setting the coordinators' objectives and deadlines, transfer them to your master planning calendar.

The back of this form lists several responsibilities. At a glance you'll be able to see who is doing what for the special event.

PLANNING AN EVENT

Title of event _____   Proposed date and time _____

Coordinator _____   Confirmed date and time _____

Phone number _____
Segment coordinators:

Program coordinator: Name _____   Phone # _____
  Responsibilities:

  Objectives: Deadlines/target dates:

_____   _____
_____   _____
_____   _____

Food coordinator: Name _____   Phone # _____
  Responsibilities:

  Objectives: Deadlines/target dates:

_____   _____
_____   _____
_____   _____

Publicity coordinator: Name _____   Phone # _____
  Responsibilities:

  Objectives: Deadlines/target dates:

_____   _____
_____   _____
_____   _____

_____ coordinator: Name _____   Phone # _____
  Responsibilities:

  Objectives: Deadlines/target dates:

_____   _____
_____   _____
_____   _____

_____ coordinator: Name _____   Phone # _____
  Responsibilities:

  Objectives: Deadlines/target dates:

_____   _____
_____   _____
_____   _____

EVENT RESPONSIBILITIES LIST

Food:
Menu
Pricing
Purchasing
Utensils
Preparation
Setup
Serving
Cleanup

Publicity:
Posters
Handouts
Announcements
Church bulletin
Media advertisements

Program:
Special speaker(s)
Scripture reading
Printed program
Congregational involvement
Prayer
Music

Music:
Accompanist
Piano/organ availability
Recorded music
Sound system
Sheet music, hymnals, etc.

Theatre:
Scripts
Lighting
Sound
Set design
Props
Costumes
Sound effects
Director

Other:
Photographer
Location
Ticket sales
Cashier
Evaluator of event
Recording of event

Sunday School Planning

Keeping track of everything that happens in Sunday school can be a harrowing job. Not only do the leaders have to keep track of teachers, curricula, supplies, students and visitors, but new Sunday school teachers often are not familiar with effective teaching methods and the Sunday school department's procedures. The following forms guide everyone involved through the Sunday-morning maze.

The Teacher Information Sheet summarizes information about the class, curriculum and teacher, and it includes the names and phone numbers of appropriate Sunday school teachers. It should be filled out at the beginning of each quarter (or when a new teacher starts). The director of Christian education can then file it in a convenient place (other people may want copies, too).

Give copies of the Teacher Checklist to each Sunday school teacher. It reminds teachers of the arrangements they need to make in advance, and it explains procedures that will help them avoid misunderstandings or conflicts. The checklist also includes helpful hints for improving teaching skills and classroom dynamics.

SUNDAY SCHOOL PLANNING

Teacher Information Sheet

Class/grade level:

Location:

Quarter (Circle one):   Fall   Winter   Spring   Summer

Curriculum (Brief description):

Approximate class size:

Special equipment or needs:

Possible substitute teachers

Name:
Phone:

Name:
Phone:

Comments:

SUNDAY SCHOOL PLANNING

Teacher Checklist

Facilities

● Visit the classroom before your first class. Know where everything is kept.

● Find the supplies you'll need (Bibles, paper, pencils, a chalk or marker board, newsprint, erasers and so on). If something is missing, check with the superintendent.

● Follow correct procedures for signing out or reserving audio-visual and other equipment. Equipment should be reserved at least one to two weeks in advance.

● Arrange the room to match the lesson—chairs in a circle for a discussion, chairs around a table for lessons that involve writing, etc.

● Make sure the room temperature is comfortable. (Freezing students aren't always as attentive as warm ones!)

● Keep extra copies of the curriculum on hand for visitors.

● If you plan special activities for your class, tell the Sunday school superintendent and the youth minister in order to avoid schedule conflicts or misunderstandings.

● Arrange with the church office to photocopy any materials well in advance.

● If you must miss a class for some reason, tell the Sunday school superintendent and arrange for a substitute teacher (or alternate arrangements) as soon as possible.

People

● Get to know the students right away. Call them by name.

● Use a crowdbreaker to gather information about each teenager. Fill out a basic information sheet on each student for future reference.

● Attendance records are useful, but don't be hard on kids who miss a few Sundays. Instead, tell them you're glad to have them in your class.

● Encourage involvement. Follow the course outline, but don't be afraid to allow the class to pursue a tangent now and then. You might learn something valuable about your students from these diversions.

● Set up too few chairs, not too many. This makes the class seem bigger, and it emphasizes the importance of quality over quantity.

● Take time to listen.

● Give the teenagers opportunities to help in the lesson (planning, gathering supplies, leading a small group).

● Enjoy your work! The kids will know if you're not having fun, so make the class both fun and educational.

Preparation for Leading a Bible Study

Leading a Bible study often strikes terror in the hearts of new leaders, young and old alike. This form gives potential leaders a handle on some of the basic preparation.

If the leader takes time to work through this preparation form, much of the study will simply fall into place. The most common mistake an individual makes is failure to wrestle with the text *before* he or she leads others. Thorough preparation gives the leader a chance to anticipate young people's questions and helps prepare for discussions on issues related to the particular scripture.

As a youth leader, you can also provide guidance for your young people and adults who may want to lead a Bible study in your group. Introduce your potential leaders to sources such as study and interpretive Bibles, concordances and Bible dictionaries. Share materials you find on issues that interest your young people. Introduce people to audio-visual catalogs or other sources in which these issues are examined.

Ask hesitant individuals to work with you as you prepare to lead a Bible study. Encourage individuals to work as a team. Experience of any kind will lessen the fear or apprehension people may feel.

PREPARATION FOR LEADING A BIBLE STUDY

I. Bible study

A. Text: _____
(Scripture passage)

    1. What's the background of this text?

    2. What are the main themes?

    3. What is the problem, dilemma or sin here?

    4. What's the Good News or promise here?

    5. How can we respond to the Gospel?

B. Topic: _____
(Subject)

    1. Other scripture texts: (See concordance, study Bible or Bible dictionaries)

        a.

        b.

        c.

    2. Other resources: (Books, magazines, newspaper articles, pamphlets, etc.)

        a.

        b.

II. Teaching methods to be used

A. Opener   Time allowed: _____   Material _____

B. Learning part   Time allowed: _____   Material _____
    1. Leader's talk
    2. Other presentations (films, music, skits, etc.)

C. Responses   Time allowed: _____   Material _____
    1. Discussion
    2. Other learning activities

D. Closing

Meeting Evaluation

Ask young people and adults to fill out evaluation forms for your meetings. Do not be concerned if you can't get everyone to complete a form since in most instances only a representative sampling is needed.

Not all items will be relevant to a particular event. Mark only those items that pertain. Sometimes young people won't be completely honest if they have to put their names on an evaluation form. So, invite them to fill out the forms anonymously.

Evaluate immediately after your meeting or an event. Don't wait. Time seems to affect our memories.

Compile the results of the evaluations in your youth council meetings. Make changes when the evaluations indicate a change is needed. When young people see recommended changes happening, they will take future evaluations more seriously.

MEETING EVALUATION

Meeting/event:

Date:

Circle the number most appropriate to each item with:

1 = No good,   2 = Weak,   3 = Okay,   4 = Good,   5 = Great.

1. The purpose of our meeting was accomplished.   1 2 3 4 5

2. All the materials were available and ready to use.   1 2 3 4 5

3. The leaders were prepared.   1 2 3 4 5

4. The advance publicity was adequate.   1 2 3 4 5

5. Transportation was well-arranged.   1 2 3 4 5

6. We had adequate adult leadership.   1 2 3 4 5

7. Attendance was adequate.   1 2 3 4 5

8. The youth group was willing to participate in planned activities. 1 2 3 4 5

The best thing about this meeting/event:

The worst thing:

Next time, we should:

Other comments:

Evaluation completed by:

PART FIVE:

Trips and Retreats

Parent Letter for Activities

Do parents know where their kids are going with the youth group? Is the final destination all they know? And when the teenagers arrive at the bus for the trip, did they forget that the campground has no sheets or towels? Use the letter and forms on the following pages to ensure that parents are well-informed and that the kids will bring everything they need.

The Parent Letter for Activities contains just about everything a parent would want to know about a trip. It includes an itinerary, emergency phone numbers, a brief outline of rules and a list of the leaders. Adapt the letter for your own trip or retreat.

Along with the letter, include copies of the Liability Release and Parental Consent Forms (see pages 29 and 30) for parents to sign and return.

If you need a less elaborate form, complete and distribute the Trip/Retreat Information form. Complete the sections that apply to your event. Send copies to all parents whose children will participate.

The Trip Checklist ensures that everyone brings everything he or she needs for the trip. Cross out the unnecessary items and add those things essential for your trip. Mail copies of the list along with the letters to parents. The teenagers can use it to gather everything for a perfect trip.

PARENT LETTER FOR ACTIVITIES

(Sample Letter)

Dear Mr. and Mrs. Dodd,

We are excited that Tammy and Stephen can join 33 other teenagers, five sponsors and me for our trip to Disney World next month. Our trip will be filled with times of fun, worship, learning and challenge. We ask you to support this activity with your prayers.

We will be leaving by bus at 6 a.m. on June 12 from the church parking lot. Your children will need to bring all luggage to the church between 6 and 9 p.m. on June 11. (See the enclosed checklist of what they should bring.)

Toni Leavell, Bob and Jean Harris, and Connie and Carl Johnston will accompany our 35 teenagers and me. As with any event, we expect only the best from each group member, but we want to stress a couple of important guidelines:
* Teenagers must stay in groups of five or more with a sponsor at Disney World.
* No smoking, drinking or other harmful activities are allowed on the trip.

Please emphasize to your children the importance of following these few rules. If a teenager doesn't abide by these guidelines or others deemed necessary by the leaders, we will contact his or her parents immediately. Action to be taken will depend on the seriousness of the violation.

We have provided a copy of our itinerary at the end of this letter. In it you will find emergency numbers, travel dates and locations where we will be staying.

Please sign the medical authorization form and return it to me by next Sunday.

As you know, the group has been raising money for this trip all spring. So the total cost to each teenager will be $100. A deposit of $50 is due by June 1, and the balance must be paid before we leave.

When your children return to Philadelphia in the afternoon on June 19, please have transportation available. We are looking forward to a great trip!

Call me if you have any questions.

Sincerely,

Pastor Jim

Pastor Jim

Itinerary for Disney World trip

June 11	6-9 p.m.:	Luggage brought to church
June 12	6 a.m.:	Leave from church parking lot
June 12	Overnight:	(429) 555-2422 Johnson Campground
		132 Lincoln, Kingstown, NC 21340
June 13	Overnight:	(308) 555-2666 KOA Campground
		429 Oak St., Lewiston, GA 31121
June 14-17:		(305) 555-7677 Dixie Orange Campground
		22 Morgan St., Orlando, FL 20202
June 17	Overnight:	(308) 555-9864 Peterson Park Campground
		317 Maple Ave., Lyford, SC 23444
June 18	Overnight:	(429) 555-2433 St. Martin's Church
		42 Main St., Hydeberg, VA 14153
		(Pastor John Bartholomew)
June 19:		Return home

PARENT LETTER FOR ACTIVITIES

Trip/Retreat Information

Event: _____

Purpose: _____

Itinerary Date/time	Activity	Location	Phone Number
_____	_____	_____	_____
_____	_____	_____	_____
_____	_____	_____	_____
_____	_____	_____	_____
_____	_____	_____	_____
_____	_____	_____	_____
_____	_____	_____	_____
_____	_____	_____	_____

Leaders: _____
_____
_____

Sponsors: _____
_____
_____

What your child needs to take along: _____
_____
_____
_____

What your child needs to leave behind: _____
_____
_____

Rules to remember: _____
_____
_____
_____

Cost: _____

Method of payment: _____

Remember, be at the _____ at _____ on _____
if you're coming with us! See you there!

PARENT LETTER FOR ACTIVITIES

Trip Checklist

Destination:

_____ Bible

_____ Proper clothing and shoes

_____ Swimsuit

_____ Rain gear

_____ Notebook, pencil

_____ Post cards, stamps, addresses

_____ Toothbrush, toothpaste and other toilet articles

_____ Camera and film

_____ Insect repellent

_____ Plastic bags for wet or soiled clothing

_____ Teddy bear

_____ Books to read

_____ Jacket

_____ Handkerchief

_____ Sunglasses

_____ Suntan lotion/sun screen

_____ Towel

_____ Washcloth

_____ Sleeping bag

_____ Pillow

_____ Medical release form/permission slip

_____ Trip contract

_____ An open heart to let God work in you during this retreat time

NO RADIOS, TAPE PLAYERS OR CD PLAYERS, PLEASE.

Lodging Request

Youth group travel is a powerful youth ministry tool. The biblical examples time and again show God at work with people while they were on the road. One cannot think of Abraham, Joseph, Moses, David, Jesus and Paul out of the context of travel. You probably know people whose lives were significantly changed during youth retreats, trips or mission tours.

Decide where you'd like to go on your next youth group trip. Locate churches or Christian colleges near your destination and along the way. Many are willing to open their facilities to traveling youth groups. Some church youth groups may even want to meet with your group as you pass through.

Phone the churches or colleges where you decide you would like to stay. Give as much advance notice as possible. Identify yourself and your youth group. Briefly explain the purpose for your call. Ask to speak to the individual who could approve your request.

Once you are speaking to the person with authority, again identify yourself and the purpose for your call. Use the Lodging Request Checklist to ask about lodging facilities on your selected dates. Inquire about rules and expectations while staying at the facility. Send a letter of confirmation as soon as you receive a reply and your plans are firm. Reconfirm your arrangements about three weeks in advance.

Arrange to inspect the facilities prior to your stay. If this is not feasible, meet with a representative of the host church upon your arrival and tour the facility. Accept responsibility for any damage done by your group, and then make sure your group members leave the facility in as good or better condition than when they found it. Be sure to ask the host representative to tour the facility with you again when you are ready to leave. If this arrangement is impossible, leave a note with any damage you are aware of or a statement that no damage was done. Be sure to thank your hosts.

Upon your return home, promptly send a thank-you note to your host churches and express your appreciation for their hospitality and extra effort. Return the favor by offering the use of your church's facilities if they need them.

LODGING REQUEST

Checklist

Information

Church/college: _____

Phone number: _____

Person talked to: _____

Dates:

   Initial phone call: _____

   Confirmation letter sent: _____

   Reply due: _____

   Reply received: _____

Address: _____

Directions (How to get there): _____

_____

_____

_____

Lodging available:

   Check one of the following:

      ☐ One large room, ☐ several small rooms, ☐ dormitory facilities with beds, ☐ other____

      Will accommodate how many? _____

      Showers available? ☐ yes ☐ no

      Fees: ☐ no charge ☐ per person, $ _____ ☐ flat rate per group, $ _____

Food service available:

   Kitchen:

      Facilities ☐ yes ☐ no

      Utensils ☐ yes ☐ no

   Host church will provide cooked meals:

      ☐ Breakfast   Cost per person, $ _____

      ☐ Lunch   Cost per person, $ _____

      ☐ Dinner   Cost per person, $ _____

   Restaurant(s) nearby:

      1. Name and type:

         Distance from church:

      2. Name and type:

         Distance from church:

Nearby attractions: Cost per person/group

      ☐ Swimming pool   _____/_____

      ☐ Roller-skating rink   _____/_____

      ☐ Bowling   _____/_____

      ☐ Tennis courts   _____/_____

      ☐ Amusement park   _____/_____

      ☐ Other List: _____ _____/_____

Regulations:

_____

_____

_____

_____

LODGING REQUEST

(Sample Letter)

Dear Rev. Masters,

Thank you again for your assistance in helping us formulate our plans for this summer's youth group trip. To confirm our conversation of March 15, our group of 22 young people and four adults plan to arrive on June 12 at 5 p.m. We understand that your youth group will provide a dinner of hot dogs, chips and dips, desserts and drinks for $2 per person. After dinner the young people from both groups will clean up the kitchen and spend the evening at the local swimming pool, which you have reserved for $25 for the evening.

After swimming, our group will retire with sleeping bags to a large room in your church basement. We understand that the young people can use the restrooms in the basement plus the ones at the top of the staircase. We will also have access to your kitchen facilities and serving dishes for breakfast and will be responsible for leaving them clean and in order. Since we must leave at 7 a.m. on June 13, we will lock all doors and leave the key on the counter under the telephone. Thank you for your help and generous assistance in making this trip one we are all looking forward to.

We will contact you again about three weeks ahead of time to make sure these plans are still satisfactory. I have enclosed the check for $25 to reserve the swimming pool. It is made out to Lackland Parks and Recreation District, as you requested. Thank you for making all of these special arrangements. We are looking forward to meeting you and your young people.

In appreciation,

Danielle

Danielle Eggert
Youth minister

Menu/Shopping List

One of the few certainties about teenagers is that they are always hungry. To make sure you won't have a major crisis when you try to satisfy their voracious appetites, plan your meals and cooking responsibilities ahead of time.

Check the Personal Information forms (see pages 118 and 119) or let the kids brainstorm about what they would like to eat at the activity. Once suggestions are made, work with your group to plan the menus. Check recipes and make a list of ingredients you will need. Add to this list any cooking utensils or supplies you will need to prepare and serve the meal.

Once you know everything you need, check ingredients you have on hand. Look over the Retreat Site Evaluation Checklist form (see page 86) to see which cooking supplies are provided by the retreat center. If possible, arrange to borrow needed items.

Now check to see what ingredients and supplies you still need, and prepare your shopping list. After all your meals are planned and the shopping lists are prepared, combine the lists and purchase needed items.

If you plan ahead, you can consult the ads in your local paper to purchase items at the best prices. If a freezer is available, you can even purchase some perishable items and store them until you need them.

MENU/SHOPPING LIST

(Sample)

Activity: Retreat
Location: Church basement—Oak Ridge Church
Number of people: 12

Day: Monday
Meal: Breakfast
Chef: David E.

Menu	Ingredients	Amount needed	Currently available
Pancakes/syrup	Pancake mix	2 (2 lb. boxes)	1 box
Sausage	Milk	5 ½ C	
Orange juice	Eggs	8	
Milk	Oil	1 C	
Coffee	Oleo	3 sticks	
	Syrup	2 (12 oz. bottles)	1 (12 oz. bottle)
	Sausage	4 lbs. sausage links	(Susan's dad will supply)
	Orange juice	2 (32 oz. cans)	1 (32 oz. can)
	Milk	2 gal.	
	Coffee	1 c (auto-drip)	¼ lb.

Cooking supplies needed	Available	Not available	Shopping list
Stove with burners	Yes		Pancake mix
Griddle		Borrow	1 (2 lb. box)
Pancake turner	Yes		Milk 3 gal.
Skillet with lid	Yes		Eggs 1 doz.
Gallon pitchers (2)		Borrow	Oil 1 (8 oz. bottle)
Coffeepot	Yes		Oleo 1 lb.
Plates	Yes		Syrup 1 (12 oz. bottle)
Silverware	Yes		Orange juice
Dishcloths	Yes		1 (32 oz. can)
Detergent	Yes		Paper towels 1 roll
Paper towels		Purchase	

Purchase/Borrow	Where/From whom?
Griddle	Kay, Jackie
Gallon pitchers	Rick, Katrina
Paper towels	purchase

MENU/SHOPPING LIST

Activity: Day:
Location: Meal:
Number of people: Chef:

Menu	Ingredients	Amount needed	Currently available

Cooking supplies needed	Available	Not available	Shopping list

Purchase/Borrow	Where/From whom?

Retreat Planning Checklist

Planning a retreat requires time and attention to a myriad of details. To ease your retreat planning, start planning at least six months prior to the date. That way you can organize manageable amounts of responsibility into a relaxed pace rather than squeeze all of your plans into a few weeks.

Follow this planning checklist to help you organize your retreats. The time line is a guide to help you with your planning. Spread responsibilities over that time period to fit your needs.

RETREAT PLANNING CHECKLIST

Six months before

_____ Prepare retreat budget; secure appropriate church board approval.
_____ Recruit adult volunteers.
_____ Provide job descriptions.
_____ Select a retreat steering committee of kids and adults.
_____ Set a purpose and theme for the retreat.
_____ Visit various retreat centers, then choose the site. Use the Retreat Site Evaluation Checklist (see page 86) for important questions on facilities, equipment, etc.
_____ Schedule dates and times for the retreat. Check dates with kids. Avoid homecoming, prom and other major school events.
_____ Organize registration. Decide details such as price, deposit, maximum and minimum number of participants, sign-up procedures and deadlines.
_____ Brainstorm for publicity ideas such as fliers, bulletin boards, posters, newsletters and so on.
_____ Assign a publicity coordinator.
_____ Begin publicity.

Four months before

_____ Involve every youth group member by setting up task forces for all aspects of the retreat such as games, refreshments, food, devotions and so on.
_____ Brainstorm ideas for sessions.

- Session #1:
  Instructor:
  Time:
  Materials:

- Session #2:
  Instructor:
  Time:
  Materials:

- Session #3:
  Instructor:
  Time:
  Materials:

_____ Brainstorm game ideas.

- Activity #1:
  Who will lead:
  Time:
  Materials:

- Activity #2:
  Who will lead:
  Time:
  Materials:

(over)

- Activity #3:
  Who will lead:
  Time:
  Materials:

_____ Brainstorm devotions and worship ideas

- Topic #1:
  Leader:
  Time:
  Material:

- Topic #2:
  Leader:
  Time:
  Material:

- Topic #3:
  Leader:
  Time:
  Material:

_____ Contact all leaders for sessions and games.
_____ Continue publicity.
_____ Review and list behavioral expectations and consequences.

Behavior	Consequences

_____ Determine transportation needs; secure insurance.

Two months before

_____ Recruit drivers. List names, phone numbers and the numbers of kids they can transport.
Name of driver _____ Phone _____ # Kids _____
Name of driver _____ Phone _____ # Kids _____
Name of driver _____ Phone _____ # Kids _____
_____ Organize refreshments and food (is it supplied by the retreat center, or must your youth group supply its own?)

- Friday evening
  Food needs:
  Who'll supply:
  Who'll cook:
  Who'll clean up:

(continued)

- Saturday morning
  Food needs:
  Who'll supply:
  Who'll cook:
  Who'll clean up:

- Saturday noon
  Food needs:
  Who'll supply:
  Who'll cook:
  Who'll clean up:

- Saturday evening
  Food needs:
  Who'll supply:
  Who'll cook:
  Who'll clean up:

- Sunday morning
  Food needs:
  Who'll supply:
  Who'll cook:
  Who'll clean up:

_____ Double-check registrations. If low, step up publicity.
_____ Prepare list of things to bring (see Retreat Checklist page 83).
_____ Prepare schedule.
_____ Distribute and collect liability forms for participants (see pages 29 and 30).
_____ Plan a parents meeting to inform them about retreat details.

Immediately before
_____ Contact all leaders; be sure they're prepared.
_____ Contact retreat site. Double-check reservation.
_____ Contact drivers.
_____ Distribute and collect Conduct Covenants for kids (see page 91).
_____ Collect all supplies.
_____ Collect all food.
_____ Check all vehicles for safety.
_____ Prepare a first-aid kit. Bring it!

During the retreat
_____ Pay rest of registration fee at retreat site.
_____ Post and follow the schedule.
_____ Plan regular discussions with volunteers to review each day.
_____ Guide daily devotions and prayer.
_____ Ask kids and volunteers to evaluate the retreat (see Retreat Evaluation form, page 88).
_____ Be sure everyone helps with cleanup.

After the retreat
_____ Reimburse drivers for gas.
_____ Meet with volunteers, steering committee and task forces to read evaluations and evaluate the retreat.
_____ Plan appropriate follow-up programming for needs discovered at retreat.
_____ List recommendations for the next retreat.
_____ Send thank-you notes to all who helped.

Retreat Checklists

Some retreat sites supply bedding and food; you simply pay a registration fee. Other sites supply cots and a kitchen, but you need to provide bedding and food. Some sites have running water; others are very rustic!

Call ahead to confirm these details, then adapt the checklist to fit your needs. Make copies to give to members and volunteers so nobody is caught unprepared.

Leaders have the extra responsibility of being in charge. Note the additional checklist of items leaders should bring. Circle the items you'll need for the retreat. For example, will you use newsprint and markers, or does the retreat site supply a chalkboard, chalk and erasers? If you need newsprint and markers, circle them and check them off when you have them packed. In the space labeled "Other," list additional items you'll need to bring.

RETREAT CHECKLIST

Participants
(What to bring)

Retreat location: _____

Theme: _____

Dates: _____

Phone number of site: _____

_____ Bible

_____ Proper clothing and shoes

_____ Swimsuit

_____ Rain gear

_____ Notebook, pencil

_____ Toothbrush, toothpaste and other toilet articles

_____ Camera and film

_____ Insect repellent

_____ Plastic bags for wet or soiled clothing

_____ Jacket

_____ Handkerchief

_____ Sunglasses

_____ Suntan lotion/sun screen

_____ Towel

_____ Washcloth

_____ Sleeping bag

_____ Pillow

_____ Teddy bear

_____ Medical release form/permission slip

_____ Retreat contract

_____ An open heart to let God work in you during this retreat time

NO RADIOS, TAPE PLAYERS OR CD PLAYERS, PLEASE.

RETREAT CHECKLIST

Additional Items for Leaders

_____ Copies of retreat schedule

_____ Names and phone numbers of drivers

_____ First-aid supplies

_____ Evaluation forms

_____ Money to pay balance of retreat site registration fee

_____ Records and record player/tapes and tape player

_____ Films and projector/video and equipment

_____ Newsprint roll ends/pads

_____ Markers

_____ Supplies for games

_____ Supplies for sessions

_____ Refreshments

_____ Extension cord

_____ Adapters

_____ Overhead projector

_____ Name tags (and pins, if needed)

_____ Masking tape

_____ Other:

Retreat Site Evaluation Checklist

Have you ever taken your kids to a retreat site only to find there were no electrical outlets or running water? Have you ever gone to a camp expecting the bedding to be supplied and it wasn't?

Avoid the unexpected by carefully evaluating a retreat site before you choose it. The best way to determine if a retreat site is good for your group is to visit it in person. Another good idea is to send a copy of this checklist to a friend near the prospective retreat center and have him or her "scout" the place for you. Finally, whenever you go to a camp or retreat center for non-youth group events, take this checklist along. That way you'll have the information when you need it.

RETREAT SITE EVALUATION CHECKLIST

_____
(Name of site)

Characteristic	Poor	Fair	Good	Great!	Explain
1. Location (Is it close to church? easy to get to?)					
2. Condition of building					
3. Facilities • Restrooms (Do they supply towels? soap? showers?) • Kitchen (Does it have a stove? a refrigerator? cooking utensils? supplies?) • Bedrooms (Do they supply bedding? cots? separate rooms? one large room? cabins?) • Meeting rooms (Are they large enough? Are chairs provided? Is there a fireplace? piano?) • Electrical outlets (Are there enough? Do you need adapters? extension cords?)					
4. Affordable					
5. Nearby recreational opportunities (Would you have access to a lake? a stream? trails? a pool? playing fields?)					
6. Game equipment (Does the camp supply equipment for basketball? softball? soccer? cross-country skiing?)					
7. Program equipment (Does it have movie screens and projectors? slide projectors? stereo equipment? microphones?)					
8. Food (Will the camp supply? cook?)					
9. Overall evaluation of the site					

Retreat Evaluation

Remember to evaluate each retreat. By simply passing out evaluation forms and pencils and having kids answer a few brief questions, you'll learn which activities went well, which activities were especially meaningful, which activities did not go as well, and which activities you should never plan again.

Personalize this evaluation form by filling in your own retreat activities and sessions in question number five.

RETREAT EVALUATION

Rate each area by responding with a number from 1 to 5 (1 = not good; 5 = great). Answer each question honestly.

1. How well did the retreat meet your expectations?   1   2   3   4   5
   - What expectations were met?

   - What expectations were not met?

2. How much did you grow because of the retreat?   1   2   3   4   5
   - What did you learn about yourself?

3. How much do you think others grew as a result of the retreat?   1   2   3   4   5
   - What did you learn about others?

4. How well did the retreat run?   1   2   3   4   5
   - What activities did you like?

   - What activities could be improved?

5. How did you feel about each of the sessions?

Friday

Crowdbreaker	1	2	3	4	5
Session #1	1	2	3	4	5
Session #2	1	2	3	4	5
Movie Time	1	2	3	4	5

Saturday

Breakfast	1	2	3	4	5
Session #3	1	2	3	4	5
Lunch	1	2	3	4	5
Session #4	1	2	3	4	5
Dinner	1	2	3	4	5
Talent Show	1	2	3	4	5

Sunday

Breakfast	1	2	3	4	5
Worship	1	2	3	4	5

6. Other observations:

Conduct Covenants

Rules should never be the focal point of a youth group or youth event. Good rules remain in the background. They provide structure and limits so group members can live and work together in a positive Christian environment. The following guidelines will help you establish effective rules for your youth activities and events:

Be positive. Expect the best. Use positive discipline that teaches rather than puts down a young person. Use consequences directed at the violation rather than the individual. Express your love for your young people by following through with prescribed consequences.

Be precise. Ask teenagers and adults to work together to set up rules both can live with. Say what you mean. Keep your list short, but state the essential rules with their consequences so that everyone can understand them.

Be prepared. Be sure everyone understands these rules *before* your activities begin. Present a yearly meeting each fall for young people and their parents to explain the general rules you will use. Ask parents and teenagers to sign a covenant so that everyone will know what is expected from the beginning.

Have another meeting for both young people and their parents to explain rules and consequences prior to special trips or activities. Print the rules in the registration materials for each event as a reminder of what to expect.

Provide for adequate adult supervision. One good rule is to have one adult per five youth. If you have 10 girls and 10 boys, try to have two men and two women to help supervise your group. Adjust this guideline to fit your particular group.

Permit responsible young people to supervise the group's discipline as much as possible. Adults' responsibility should be primarily support.

Control the environment by scheduling specific activities. Large blocks of unscheduled, unsupervised, unplanned time often invite problems.

Decide who owns the problem before you say or do anything. Ask yourself two questions: "Is this something I personally disapprove of, but something that is within the limits of the rules?" and "Is this behavior a clear violation of our group's rules?" Sometimes the problem is with our own attitudes and prejudices.

Always get the facts from those directly involved. Don't ask your young people, "Is this true?" or "Can you tell me more?" Ask your young people to give you the facts about the situation. Let them know that the trip or activity cannot continue until the situation is resolved.

Love rules all. The ultimate question is "What is the loving thing to do?" Christian love is tough love that seeks to discipline, teach and correct within the biblical norms. There are times when the letter of the law must give way to the spirit of love. Know your young people; know their needs and circumstances. Sometimes your discipline has to first "speak" to the individual so he or she can know that you care. Consistency is important, but people are more important.

CONDUCT COVENANTS

(Sample)

A team of young people and adults made the following set of rules for a weekend retreat. The rules were so popular that they've been used for many years.

THE TEN COMMANDMENTS

I. *Thy car shall not be used during the retreat.*

II. *Thy body shall not leave the retreat grounds.*

III. *Thy body shall not be with the body of the opposite sex in the opposite sex's room.*

IV. *Thou shall not puff a weed of any kind, space out on any pills or drink alcohol during the retreat.*

V. *Thou shall report any injury immediately to the sponsor.*

VI. *Thou shall not burn any fireworks.*

VII. *Thou shall not trespass on thy neighbor's body or self-esteem.*

VIII. *Thou shall be at events on time.*

IX. *Thou shall observe all camp rules.*

X. *Thou shall be okay.*

Anyone caught breaking these rules will be talked with. After considering the seriousness of the transgression, the youth council has the option of asking that person's parents to come and take him or her home.

CONDUCT COVENANTS

Rules Worksheet

Use the form below to formulate rules acceptable to both young people and adults. This simple format will help you communicate your activity's rules and consequences to everyone who will participate.

Rules   **Consequences**

Travel Expense Log

When you're on the road, it's difficult to remember how much money you spend on youth group supplies, food and transportation. This expense log should help. It is a simple, yet effective tool for recording expenses related to your travels in youth ministry.

This form has space for two days of expenses on each page. Copies of this form will fit neatly into a three-ring binder you can take on trips, retreats, outings and other youth group events. You may prefer to reduce the size of the form so it will fit into a smaller notebook for easier carrying.

The space for descriptions includes the heading ''Receipt.'' You can use this space to indicate whether a receipt was kept for that particular item. Attach an envelope to your expense log notebook for storing your receipts.

When you keep a record of your expenses and receipts in your expense log, you can use that information to complete expense reports and fill out check requests as needed. This information can also help with future youth group budgeting.

TRAVEL EXPENSE LOG

Record of expenses for _____/_____/_____ Completed by _____
(Month   day   year)

Food:
Item	Purchased from	Amount $	Receipt

Lodging:
Description	Amount $	Receipt

Transportation:
Vehicle: Cities visited:
Mileage:
Gas: $ _____   Other transportation costs: $ _____

(Keep all receipts. Use this record for noting all expenses for the youth group.)

Record of expenses for _____/_____/_____ Completed by _____
(Month   day   year)

Food:
Item	Purchased from	Amount $	Receipt

Lodging:
Description	Amount $	Receipt

Transportation:
Vehicle: Cities visited:
Mileage:
Gas: $ _____   Other transportation costs: $ _____

(Keep all receipts. Use this record for noting all expenses for the youth group.)

PART SIX:

Fund Raising

Planning a Fund Raiser

The success of a fund-raising event is directly related to how well the event was planned and publicized. Use the planning form that follows as a starting point and reference tool for your fund raisers. Examples of fund raisers are listed on the form for reference.

The planning section is particularly important for recording ways to publicize your activity. Include specific information about the type of publicity you will use. If you decide to use posters or fliers, decide who will prepare these items and when and where they will be placed for distribution. If you decide to advertise in newspapers or the church newsletter, find out when and where you must submit the copy for your event.

Record the source for your fund raiser. Was it a kid's idea? Was it suggested by a particular parent or youth leader? Was it original? Did you find it in an issue of GROUP Magazine or some other publication?

Many youth groups keep a photo record of their fund-raising events. Be sure to designate who will take responsibility for photographing the fund raiser.

To use this form as a reference tool, it is important to record the actual expenses and income for each event. Keeping a file of these forms builds a solid history of your fund raising. By referring to these forms, you won't repeat events too often. You'll also know which events were successful and could be repeated.

PLANNING A FUND RAISER

Purpose of the fund raiser: _____

_____

_____

Dollar goal: $ _____

Type of fund raiser: _____

Work for cash	**Prepared sales**	**Food fund raisers**	**Marathons**
Carwash	Candy	Bake sale	Walk-a-thon
Yardwork	Gift wrap	All-church dinner	Rock-a-thon
Slave day	Candles	Dinner theatre	Work-a-thon
Wash windows	Posters	Cookie auction	Volleyball-a-thon
Housecleaning		Meal delivery	**Other**
House painting			Singing telegrams
			Raffles

How will the fund raiser work? _____

_____

What will you call it? _____

_____

Planning section

Location _____

Date(s) _____

Publicity _____

(What) _____ (When) _____ (Where) _____

(What) _____ (When) _____ (Where) _____

(What) _____ (When) _____ (Where) _____

Supplies needed_____

_____

Estimated expenses _____

_____

Source of the fund-raising idea _____

Who will take photographs of the event?_____

Expense report

Actual expenses: $ _____

Total income: $ _____

Net dollars raised: $ _____

Is this a good fund raiser to repeat? _____ Explain: _____

_____

Fund-Raising Sponsor Sheet

Many youth groups' fund-raising events call for community sponsorship of young people in marathons of time, distance or endurance. This form allows sponsors to pledge by the hour, mile or other unit as determined by the event.

A very important ingredient of this form is the section explaining the purpose for which the money will be used. Take care that you clearly identify the fund-raising goal.

Each young person should complete and duplicate this form. One copy will stay with the coordinator to keep track of each participant's pledges, and the other copy will be used by the participant to collect his or her pledged dollars.

Now you can organize walk-a-thons, rock-a-thons and how-many-pieces-of-pizza-do-you-think-I-can-eat-a-thons. Use a copy of this same form to list total pledges and amounts collected by each participant. Award prizes to the person who collects the most money for the fund-raising effort.

FUND-RAISING SPONSOR SHEET

Event: _____

Organization: _____

To raise money for: _____

_____

_____

Date: _____ Time: _____

Location: _____

Coordinator: _____

Participant: _____

Name: _____

Address: _____

_____

Phone number: _____ Age: _____

Pledge amount is per: ☐ hour ☐ mile ☐ other_____

Sponsor's Name	Address	Amount pledged per unit	Total amount collected
		Total amount pledged (per unit)	Total amount collected

Total units completed by participant _____ ☐ hours ☐ miles ☐ other _____

Approved by _____

Fund-Raising Accountability Form

Sooner or later every youth group needs to raise funds for workcamps, retreats, summer trips, mission support, etc. These activities are valuable not only for the money raised, but more importantly for the opportunities they provide young people to serve their church and community and to build community among themselves.

To ensure fairness and maintain the community building that has been done, accountability is important, especially when you distribute funds. The following form is based on a point system in which credit is earned not only through fund-raising activities, but also through participation in the life of the church.

Write the month in the blank at the top of the page. List the names of all teenagers in your group in the column on the left. Record and date meetings and fund-raising activities in the spaces at the bottom of the page and record points in the appropriate spaces. At the end of your fund raising, total the points for each individual.

Some groups may decide to let individuals share equally in the distribution of funds if they reach a certain total. Other groups may choose to distribute funds according to an individual's points earned in relation to the total number of points possible. Whichever way you decide to distribute funds, remember to maintain the positive community building your group has already established.

FUND-RAISING ACCOUNTABILITY FORM

(Sample)

JANUARY
(Month)

	Name	Points												Point Totals
1.	Jane B.	1	1	1	1		1	1	1		1	3	1	12
2.	David D.		1		1			1			1			4
3.	Ann O.	1	1	1			1	1		1	1		1	8
4.	Jackie M.	1	1	1	1	2	1	1	1	1	1	3	1	15
5.	Cindy P.					2						3		5
6.	Mike S.		1		1			1	1		1	3		8
7.	Alice T.		1		1			1	1		1	3		8
8.	Arnie W.	1		1		2	1		1				1	7
9.														
10.														
11.														
12.														
13.														
14.														
15.														
16.														
17.														
18.														
19.														
20.														

Meeting/Activity   Date

Key
Youth meeting _1_ pts
Sunday school _1_ pts
Fund raiser _2_ pts
Other
Visitation _1_ pts
Youth Sunday _3_ pts
_____ pts

Column headings (Date / Meeting/Activity):
- Youth Meeting 1/3/87
- Sunday School 1/4/87
- Youth Meeting 1/10/87
- Sunday School 1/11/87
- Cleanup Day 1/17/87
- Youth Meeting 1/17/87
- Sunday School 1/18/87
- Visitation 1/21/87
- Youth Meeting 1/24/87
- Sunday School 1/25/87
- Youth Sunday 1/25/87
- Youth Meeting 1/25/87

FUND-RAISING ACCOUNTABILITY FORM

_____
(Month)

	Name	Points												Point Totals
1.														
2.														
3.														
4.														
5.														
6.														
7.														
8.														
9.														
10.														
11.														
12.														
13.														
14.														
15.														
16.														
17.														
18.														
19.														
20.														

Meeting/Activity Date

Key
Youth meeting
_____ pts
Sunday school
_____ pts
Fund raiser
_____ pts
Other
_____
_____ pts
_____
_____ pts
_____
_____ pts

PART SEVEN:

Planning

Life Planning Inventory

Even if we don't write them, most of us have hopes and dreams for our lives. Some of us hope to marry and have kids. Others hope to earn a particular promotion. Many have specific educational and career goals. Still others dream of finding that special house or moving to the mountains.

This form encourages youth workers to examine or evaluate their hopes and dreams. A minimal amount of categorizing has been done here. The idea is simply to launch the process.

Here are some guidelines for planning your life and attaining your goals:

1. Be *specific*. For example, getting married is a good goal, but too general. What are some steps that might help you accomplish this goal? Perhaps you need to meet more young women or men who are attractive to you in thoughts as well as looks. Involve yourself in groups that interest you, and look for individuals who express mutual interests and goals.

2. Make your goals *measurable*. For example, to get in shape is a great goal, but how do you measure it? Maybe you can walk every other day for a week, or perhaps you can remove sugar from your diet after noon. No matter what you try, make sure you can measure your success.

3. Have a *plan*. Decide exactly how you will initiate, implement and evaluate your hopes and dreams. Write your plan on paper and check it every day to see if you are "on the right track."

4. Be *realistic* and *graceful* to yourself. After all, we are saved by grace. It's easy to set yourself up for failure and guilt. Your goals should be realistic as well as challenging.

5. Keep your goals *visible*, and look at them once in a while. There is nothing magical about setting goals, especially if you can't remember them.

6. Develop an *accountability* system for yourself. Friends and (or) family members who know your hopes and dreams can help tremendously. Prayer helps too!

7. *Prioritize*. Sooner or later your plans and dreams will conflict. Blind pursuit of minor goals can sabotage the success of your more important dreams.

8. *Update* your dreams and plans annually. Our goals when we are 25 will probably be different when we're 35. We may discover that our plans were not *God's* plans!

LIFE PLANNING INVENTORY

_____
(Name)

_____
(Date)

Professional goals:	Personal goals:
1.	1.
2.	2.
3.	3.
4.	4.
5.	5.

After you've listed your goals, ask yourself:

1. Are they *specific?*

2. Are they *measurable?*

3. Are they *realistic?*

Time Planners
Daily, Weekly, Yearly

Time is a precious commodity for youth leaders. Activities not written down are easily forgotten in the rush of daily ministerial duties. A daily, weekly and yearly planner can help you schedule your time and remember details.

Keep a log of your work to help you organize and use your time wisely. The log can provide a spiritual journal of your youth ministry and help you account for the time spent with your ministry, your family, your goals and objectives, and your relationship with Christ.

Use the daily planner to list your appointments. In the "needs" column, jot the stuff to bring, things to remember, etc. for the appointment. Jot down tasks that weren't completed the day before, tasks you need to do today and tasks that are coming up. Most importantly, plan time for family and devotions *before* you schedule other activities.

Use the weekly planner to see seven days at a glance. Write down activities, meetings, needs and other information you should know for each day.

Use the yearly plan-and-do calendar to record long-range plans. Each month write down activities and events you need to plan as well as those you need to do. For example, in January, *plan* February's Valentine party, *do* the winter carnival. In February, *plan* the Easter breakfast, *do* the Valentine's party and so on.

Purchase or make a large calendar where you can record all the year's activities at a glance. Schedule big events and activities well in advance. At the beginning of each week, check your calendar and make a list of the important items that need your attention during the coming week. Make sure youth activities and all-church functions do not conflict. Remember to put youth activities on the total church calendar as soon as possible so other activities do not conflict with the young people's plans.

Share your planning logs with a spiritual adviser or a close Christian friend. Ask that person for input on how you might become more effective in the use of your time.

Remember you may accomplish only part of your tasks each day. None of us can do everything. Look to God for strength to accomplish your most important goals.

TIME PLANNER

Daily Planner

_____
(Date)

Time	Description	Needs	Yesterday's tasks
7:00			
8:00			
9:00			**Today's tasks**
10:00			
11:00			
12:00			**What's ahead**
1:00			
2:00			**Family time/devotions**
3:00			
4:00			
5:00			
6:00			
7:00			
8:00			
9:00			
10:00			
11:00			
12:00			

TIME PLANNER

Weekly Planner
For the week of _____ to _____

Day	Activity/meeting	Needs	Other
Monday			
Tuesday			
Wednesday			
Thursday			
Friday			
Saturday			
Sunday			

TIME PLANNER

Yearly Plan-and-Do Calendar

_____
(Year)

January	February	March
Plan:	Plan:	Plan:
Do:	Do:	Do:

April	May	June
Plan	Plan:	Plan:
Do:	Do:	Do:

July	August	September
Plan:	Plan:	Plan:
Do:	Do:	Do:

October	November	December
Plan:	Plan:	Plan:
Do:	Do:	Do:

Less-Stress Checklist

Planning has only one price: time. But lack of planning costs so much more: stress, disorganization, "last minutitis," surprises, anger, disappointments, mediocrity, chronic crises, etc.

The Less-Stress Checklist helps identify sources of stress in your life. Chances are that the more times you answer "yes," the more you are in control of your life. If you have 15 or more "no" responses, you probably do not have control of your work.

Share this checklist with volunteers and other key adults in your church's youth ministry. Use it as a starting point for setting priorities and clarifying values, goals and objectives.

LESS-STRESS CHECKLIST

	Yes	No
1. Is my discretionary time used for high-priority tasks?	☐	☐
2. Have I set goals and objectives for my ministry?	☐	☐
3. Have I set *personal* goals and objectives?	☐	☐
4. Does the church have written goals, objectives and policies for youth ministry?	☐	☐
5. Have I read and do I understand these goals, objectives and policies?	☐	☐
6. Do I have a clearly written job description that is mutually agreeable to my supervisor(s) and myself?	☐	☐
7. Is my planning geared to achieve these goals and objectives?	☐	☐
8. Do I clarify and check the reality of my planning with the proper staff and committees?	☐	☐
9. Do I seek the counsel of trusted outside advisers?	☐	☐
10. Do I meet regularly with at least one trusted colleague who knows my goals and objectives, and holds me accountable for them?	☐	☐
11. Do I invest at least 15 to 30 minutes a day in planning?	☐	☐
12. Do I invest at least 15 to 30 minutes a day in prayer?	☐	☐
13. Have I identified my most productive time of the day?	☐	☐
14. Do I use this time to tackle my most vital tasks?	☐	☐
15. Do I *manage* my interruptions by anticipating the times most prone to them?	☐	☐
16. Do I have the secretary screen calls and take messages for me?	☐	☐
17. Do I limit the time I spend on phone calls?	☐	☐
18. Does the youth ministry have an organizational chart?	☐	☐
19. Do all staff members, committees, volunteers and student leaders have clearly written job descriptions?	☐	☐
20. Do I regularly (at least quarterly) review performance of key youth ministry people?	☐	☐
21. Do I provide opportunities for key people to grow?	☐	☐
22. Do I continually research young people's needs?	☐	☐
23. Have I clearly identified my own needs and wants?	☐	☐
24. Do I assertively guard my own time, providing necessary nourishment to feed my needs?	☐	☐
25. Do I courageously say no to those things that don't contribute *totally* to my life goals?	☐	☐
26. Do I spend time *only* on the TV shows, movies, music, books, magazines and other media that nourish my needs and contribute to my goals?	☐	☐
27. Do I record expenses, notes, to-do lists, phone numbers, etc., in *only one* place (calendar, Day-Timer, etc.)?	☐	☐
28. Do I accept 100 percent of the responsibility for my communication?	☐	☐

(over)

		Yes	No
29.	Do I have a family budget that reflects my values and goals?	☐	☐
30.	Do I provide punctual feedback to others' questions and concerns?	☐	☐
31.	Do I pay my bills on time?	☐	☐
32.	Have I protected my family as much as possible in the event of my unexpected death?	☐	☐
33.	Have I disciplined myself to plan ahead in youth ministry, thus reducing the number of last minute scrambles before meetings, events, trips, retreats, etc.?	☐	☐
34.	Have I planned for at least two significant continuing-education opportunities in the next year that apply directly toward my life goals?	☐	☐
35.	Have I asked myself within the past week: "What have I been doing that I should do less of? What do I need to do more of?"	☐	☐
36.	Do I start and end the meetings I lead on time?	☐	☐
37.	Do I prepare a written agenda and distribute it at least four days before a meeting?	☐	☐
38.	Do I delegate responsibility *and* authority for tasks, making sure that I clearly communicate what I want and that I provide the training the helper(s) will need?	☐	☐
39.	In times of seemingly overwhelming work, do I ask myself: "How important is this task? Will it matter a year from now?"	☐	☐
40.	I have memorized the "Serenity Prayer," which is:	☐	☐

God grant me
the SERENITY
to accept the things
I cannot change,
the COURAGE to change
the things I can,
and the WISDOM to know
the difference.

Total yes _____

Total no _____

Prayer List

Prayer is our way of communicating with God. We use prayer not only to ask for God's presence in our own lives, but also to ask for God's involvement in the lives of others. God is concerned about all of his creation. He's ready to listen to our concerns, and he's also willing to provide answers if we listen to him.

The following principles will help you each time you set aside time to pray for your youth group, your family and yourself.

1. Arrange for a specific time and place to pray. Discipline yourself to keep your "appointment with God."

2. Find out others' needs and write them on your Prayer List. The more specific your concerns, the better prepared you will be for your prayer time.

3. Focus on God and his will. Ask for God's guidance and peace, both for yourself and for the others for whom you are praying.

4. Study Bible passages about prayer such as John 17, Philippians 4:6-7 and 1 Thessalonians 5:16-18. Remember Jesus' words, "I will be with you always" (Matthew 28:20).

5. Direct specific requests to God. Go through the needs on your Prayer List one by one. Be assured that God hears you and knows what you need.

6. Be silent and take time to listen to God. "He will teach you all things" (John 14:26). Open yourself to his direction and compassion for others.

7. Put your Prayer List in a place where you will see it often—in your daily planner, on the dashboard of your car, on your mirror at home. Use those moments when you are waiting on the phone, sitting at a stoplight or brushing your teeth to remember those for whom you are concerned. God hears all our prayers and may provide answers at any moment if we are open to his presence.

PRAYER LIST

Write in those individuals and the specific concerns for which you need to pray. Be alert to God's presence at all times. Remember, "What is impossible with men is possible with God" (Luke 18:27).

Individual needs:

Name	Specific needs and concerns	Comments

Youth group's needs:

_____
_____
_____
_____
_____

My family's needs:

_____
_____
_____
_____
_____

Personal needs:

_____
_____
_____
_____
_____

Scripture passage that is especially meaningful to me:

_____
_____
_____

Activity and Interest Inventory

Do you know what your kids like to do? What are their interests? The following form can help you inventory the likes and dislikes of your kids in sports, activities, food, music and outdoor stuff.

Have each group member take a few minutes to complete this form. Add the individual ratings for an item and divide by the number of responses you receive to get an average rating for that item. The results of this evaluation should help you plan what foods to have at a barbecue, what music to play before a meeting, etc.

This form can also provide valuable information about your kids. File it with the Personal Information form for each of your youth group members. It can help you know how to reach a kid with a problem or how to make someone feel at ease in a one-on-one session.

Since teenagers and their interests change constantly, update this form periodically. Have your members complete it at least once a year. For best use of time, pass out this inventory with one or both of the Youth Needs Surveys.

ACTIVITY AND INTEREST INVENTORY

Name: _____ Date: _____

Age: _____

In the following lists rate each item from 1 to 10 based on your interest. Write a number in the blank to the left of each item with 1 being "Yuck" and 10 being "Great." If you feel the same about two or more different items, they can both have the same rating. If you don't have any feeling one way or another about an item, use a zero.

Sports:
_____ Basketball
_____ Baseball
_____ Softball
_____ Volleyball
_____ Football
_____ Hockey
_____ Soccer
_____ Bowling
_____ Tennis
_____ Skating
_____ Swimming

Outdoor stuff:
_____ Picnics
_____ Hiking
_____ Camping
_____ Water sports
_____ Biking
_____ Skiing
_____ Amusement park

Activities:
_____ Concerts
_____ Work projects
_____ Musicals
_____ Dinner theatre
_____ Shopping
_____ Movies
_____ Parties
_____ Progressive dinners
_____ Revivals

Food:
_____ Pizza
_____ Hamburgers
_____ Chinese
_____ Mexican
_____ Italian
_____ Hot dogs
_____ French fries
_____ Yogurt
_____ Ice cream

Musical styles:
_____ Rock
_____ Classical
_____ Jazz
_____ Country
_____ New wave
_____ Easy listening
_____ Heavy metal
_____ Christian Rock

Personal Information

Here it is. Everything you ever wanted to know about one of your young people is all on *one* sheet of paper. Well, maybe not everything. But there is a lot of information on this form. Page 1 is basic information you may need for each one of your group members. Page 2 provides a fun personality profile. Each group member can complete his or her own Personal Information sheet.

This Personal Information form serves as a base for your youth group member filing system. It keeps information on each person's family, school and medical history readily available. Simply refer to the back of the form to get a flavor of each group member's personality.

The notes section on page 1 of the form can be a valuable tool in your ministry. Use it often to record facts or thoughts about an individual's strengths, problems and needs. Record other observations. Be sure to update the form as situations change.

If you don't currently keep files on your youth group members, consider using this form. You'll be surprised how often you'll refer to it.

PERSONAL INFORMATION

(Church name)

Basic information:

Page 1

_____   _____   _____
Name   Nickname   Age

_____   _____   _____
Address   Phone number   Birth date

_____
Parents' names and work phone numbers

_____   _____
Brothers'/sisters' names and ages

_____   _____
School   Grade

_____
Interests and activities

_____   _____
Pets   Part-time job/hours of work

Medical information:

_____   _____
Health insurance company   Policy number

Allergies, special needs, etc.
_____
_____
_____

Notes: (Indicate date of entry)
_____
_____
_____
_____
_____
_____

_____   _____
Form completed by   Date

_____   _____
Updated by   Date

PERSONAL INFORMATION

Personality profile: **Page 2**

Name: _____

Complete the following statements:

1. I was born in _____ _____
                   (City)   (State)

2. My favorite food is _____

3. My favorite color is _____

4. One thing I'm good at is _____

5. Something I have difficulty with is _____

6. The kind of music I listen to is _____

7. A movie I really liked was _____

8. One of the things I really like about school is _____
_____

9. The one thing about school that I don't really like is _____
_____

10. The career I'm most interested in is _____

Mark an X on the line where you fit in the following statements:

I am: _____
         (shy   average   outgoing)

I am: _____
         (affectionate   friendly   anti-social)

Circle the more appropriate word for each of the following statements.

I am more:	a leader	a follower
I am more:	laid-back	on the go
I am more:	demanding of self and others	accepting of self and others

Youth Needs Surveys

Planning new directions for your youth ministry must be based on good information, not guesses. In order for your ministry to meet needs you must know what those needs are.

Your youth ministry team can assess fairly well your young people's needs through surveys. Following are two needs surveys for your young people to complete. Remember to maintain confidentiality concerning the survey responses. Strive to get full participation in your needs surveys.

The results of your surveys should supply you with plenty of ideas for constructing the future of your youth ministry. You'll be better equipped to set some goals, and you'll know some of the pressing issues that need to be addressed in your programming.

YOUTH NEEDS SURVEY

We're making plans for upcoming youth group programs. We want these programs to address your needs. But before we can address them, we need to know what they are. Help us by completing the following survey.

1. What are the top five worries or concerns in your life? (Check five only.)

_____ My relationship with God.   _____ My parents might die.

_____ Making and keeping friends.   _____ I might kill myself.

_____ Peer pressure.   _____ Loneliness.

_____ Drugs.   _____ Stress.

_____ Drinking.   _____ Cliques.

_____ Doing well in school.   _____ Divorce.

_____ Dealing with temptation.   _____ Self-esteem.

_____ My looks.   _____ Prayer.

_____ The future.   _____ Getting along with parents.

_____ College.   _____ Music.

_____ Nuclear war.   _____ Suicide.

_____ World hunger.   _____ Sharing my faith.

_____ Dating.   _____ Cults.

_____ Racism.   _____ Other: _____.

_____ Money.   _____ Other: _____.

2. The biggest issue or concern in my life right now is:

THANK YOU!

YOUTH NEEDS SURVEY

We're making plans for upcoming youth group programs. Help us make these plans by telling us which topics interest you. Circle a number for each item.

	INTERESTS ME										NO INTEREST
Getting along with parents.	10	9	8	7	6	5	4	3	2	1	0
Alcoholic parents.	10	9	8	7	6	5	4	3	2	1	0
Single-parent households.	10	9	8	7	6	5	4	3	2	1	0
Stepparents.	10	9	8	7	6	5	4	3	2	1	0
Making friends.	10	9	8	7	6	5	4	3	2	1	0
Relating to non-Christian friends.	10	9	8	7	6	5	4	3	2	1	0
What to do on a date.	10	9	8	7	6	5	4	3	2	1	0
How to be attractive to the opposite sex.	10	9	8	7	6	5	4	3	2	1	0
On a date, how far is too far?	10	9	8	7	6	5	4	3	2	1	0
How do I know God's will for my life?	10	9	8	7	6	5	4	3	2	1	0
What does "born again" really mean?	10	9	8	7	6	5	4	3	2	1	0
Why does God let bad things happen?	10	9	8	7	6	5	4	3	2	1	0
Coping with stress at school.	10	9	8	7	6	5	4	3	2	1	0
Cliques.	10	9	8	7	6	5	4	3	2	1	0
How to love myself.	10	9	8	7	6	5	4	3	2	1	0
Why doesn't God answer my prayers?	10	9	8	7	6	5	4	3	2	1	0
Is it wrong for Christians to drink?	10	9	8	7	6	5	4	3	2	1	0
How can Christians react to the nuclear threat?	10	9	8	7	6	5	4	3	2	1	0
Dealing with temptation.	10	9	8	7	6	5	4	3	2	1	0
What can we do about world hunger?	10	9	8	7	6	5	4	3	2	1	0
Dealing with peer pressure.	10	9	8	7	6	5	4	3	2	1	0
What will I do after high school?	10	9	8	7	6	5	4	3	2	1	0
What college should I attend?	10	9	8	7	6	5	4	3	2	1	0
What can I do about loneliness?	10	9	8	7	6	5	4	3	2	1	0
I'm scared of losing someone close to me.	10	9	8	7	6	5	4	3	2	1	0
What position should I take on abortion?	10	9	8	7	6	5	4	3	2	1	0
I worry about money.	10	9	8	7	6	5	4	3	2	1	0
Other: _____	10	9	8	7	6	5	4	3	2	1	0
Other: _____	10	9	8	7	6	5	4	3	2	1	0

THANK YOU!

PART EIGHT:

Communications

News Releases

Have you ever sent information about your group's next great event to your local newspaper, only to find that the news appears as an obscure sentence buried beneath the obituaries? Or maybe it never appeared at all.

Here are some guidelines for preparing publicity material for media use:

- Write stories that won't require excessive editing.

- Supply material that is of particular interest to the medium's audience. For example, guest speakers, concerts and other special events are more newsworthy than in-church matters.

- Be sure to include *all* the essential details—time, date, place, who and why. Many busy editors find it easier to throw away incomplete releases than to track down the missing information.

- When promoting fund raisers, always say why the group is raising money. The more specific the reason, the better.

- Submit only neatly typed, double-spaced news releases. Never send a photocopy of the release—editors like to receive original material.

- For most events, the best time to submit material is one week beforehand. It's best to deliver it in person. Many editors will remember the personal touch.

- Like it or not, today's society reads less and looks at pictures more. So whenever possible, submit black-and-white "action" photographs with your news releases. It's okay to stage these photos. For example, a leader of a group that operated a fireworks stand as a fund raiser snapped close-up photos of two young people painting the stand. (Close-ups tend to draw much more attention than a distant shot would.) Tape a piece of paper on the back of a photo identifying the people in it and describing through a sentence "caption" what they are doing.

- Always include your name and phone number at the top of the release.

- More is not always better. Do not oversaturate the editor with releases on every meeting or event. Choose those that are particularly important and give them extra attention.

- You can build your group's identity with a logo. News releases typed on typically mundane church letterhead may give a subconscious message to editors that your event will be boring. A better image-building tactic is to find an artist in your congregation and ask him or her to create a logo for your group that reflects youthfulness without diminishing the church's image.

NEWS RELEASE

(Sample)

FOR IMMEDIATE RELEASE   CONTACT: Lee Sparks
                                                                  555-3836

"Nothing But the Best" Comedy Concert Planned for Teenagers & Parents
7 p.m., Sunday, September 21

When was the last time truth made you laugh until you hurt? Faith
Evangelical Church will offer a "Nothing But the Best" comedy concert by
Ken Davis at 7 p.m. on Sunday, September 21 at the church, 2707 N.
Wilson, Centerville. Senior and junior high teenagers, their parents
and youth leaders are encouraged to attend. There is no admission
charge, and the event is open to the public.

Davis' theme for the evening will be, "You are a worthwhile
individual because that's how God created you and because he gives you
nothing but the best." This dynamic message will challenge youth and
their parents to grow in Christian faith.

Davis' energetic style and wholesome humor has made him one of the
nation's top inspirational and motivational entertainers. Davis has
appeared before large audiences and on television, and he leads
motivational seminars for hundreds of business executives and ministry
personnel. He is also a popular speaker at the annual National
Christian Youth Congress and appears at the Comedy Works in Denver.
Davis is the author of "How to Speak to Youth ... and Keep Them Awake at
the Same Time."

Newsletter Production Worksheet

Poor organization kills many promising youth newsletters after one or two issues. The first steps to publishing a consistently good newsletter are preparation and organization.

The Newsletter Production Worksheet helps you organize both the ingredients of and the contributors to the newsletter. This form uses a "formula" approach to maintain a consistent style for your newsletter.

The production schedule helps plan, schedule and track the actual process of producing the newsletter. Keep track of incoming articles, and make sure you're on schedule for printing.

Use the production costs section to determine how your budget is spent. Producing a good newsletter doesn't have to be expensive. This simple section helps you make yours more cost-effective.

Some suggestions for contents:

1. *Upcoming group activities.* Give all necessary details of who, what, where, when, why and how.

2. *Past activities.* To let those who were there enjoy reading about them; those who weren't there will know what they missed.

3. *Youth member profile.* Helps new kids become acquainted with group. A short biographical piece.

4. *Bible passage.* A short passage from a modern translation Bible.

5. *Youth leader column.* A *brief* word from the youth minister.

6. *Humor/cartoons.* Use positive humor. Group's *Youth Ministry Clip Art* offers hundreds of cartoons to add punch and color to your newsletter.

7. *Names, names, names.* Strive to get as many kids' names as possible into the newsletter. We all love to see our names in print.

NEWSLETTER PRODUCTION WORKSHEET

General information

Issue date: _____   Volume: _____   Number: _____

Number of pages: _____

Editor: _____

Contributing editors: _____

Art design: _____

Printed by: _____

Contents/Assignments

Articles	Specific topic	Author	Date assigned	Date due
Feature: _____	_____	_____	_____	_____
Upcoming activities: _____	_____	_____	_____	_____
Past activities: _____	_____	_____	_____	_____
Youth member profile: _____	_____	_____	_____	_____
Bible passage: _____	_____	_____	_____	_____
Youth leader column: _____	_____	_____	_____	_____
Humor/cartoon: _____	_____	_____	_____	_____

Production schedule

Articles   Date received:

Copy edited by: _____   Date: _____

Copy proofread by: _____   Date: _____

Art received by: _____   Date: _____

Layout and paste-up completed by: _____   Date: _____

Date to printer: _____

Date received from printer: _____

Date addressed: _____   Date mailed: _____

Production costs

Paper $ _____

Printing $ _____

Misc. materials $ _____

Postage $ _____

Other (explain) $ _____

                         $ _____

                         $ _____

Total cost $ _____

Cost per copy $ _____

(Total expenses divided by number of copies printed)

Youth Ministry Calendar

How many times has your youth ministry team planned a really good event—only to suffer poor attendance because the kids weren't informed? A monthly Youth Ministry Calendar can help greatly to keep kids and their parents informed of upcoming activities. Calendars, along with newsletters, bulletin announcements, verbal announcements, phone calls and other communication media, will get the word out.

Calendars should list the date, time and place of your events. However, these mundane facts alone will probably not keep your calendar posted on bulletin boards or refrigerators. Include also the birthdays of kids and adult volunteers, special events at schools, and some things just for fun. *Chase's Annual Events* lists scores of non-essential dates for some fairly strange happenings.

Mail the calendar with youth newsletters or other mailings. Addressing the calendar to both parents and their children will help keep parents informed.

THE CALENDAR

MONTH _____

SUNDAY	MON	TUES	WEDNESDAY	THURS	FRIDAY	SATURDAY

Poster Production Checklist

Creative posters grab attention for events, activities, Bible studies and trips. Several steps are involved in preparing them. Follow this checklist each time you want to make posters. Let your mind go, and be creative as you dream of catchy headlines such as ''Snowball Bash'' for a winter party or ''Manic Monday Blues'' for a study on dealing with down feelings at the beginning of the week.

Vary the way you make a poster. One time make letters from construction paper; another time paint the letters; another time print your letters with markers or crayons; and another time stencil or trace the letters.

Vary the size of the letters. For example, use large letters for the headline and smaller letters for the details. Leave space around the borders, and beware of crowding too much on the poster. Aim for attractiveness.

Use drawings, magazine pictures or clip art. Ask an artistic youth group member to help you illustrate the poster. Add variety with other materials such as yarn, aluminum foil, glitter and stars. Use your creativity!

POSTER PRODUCTION CHECKLIST

Activity to publicize: _____

Dates:_____

Costs:_____

Registration information: _____

Location of activity:_____

Age: _____

Other:_____

(for horizontal poster)

(for vertical poster)

(Rough sketch of poster)

_____ Write a rough draft of the information you want to include. Say who, what, when, where and why. Don't forget the fee and sign-up information.

_____ Design a thumbnail sketch of your poster. (Use blank boxes above.)

_____ Decide on the number of posters you'll need to advertise the event. Where will you hang them? at church? at schools?

_____ Think of illustrations, clip art, magazine pictures you could use.

_____ Write an attention-grabbing headline.

_____ Choose a full piece of posterboard, or trim to a smaller size. Gather all materials such as markers, paint, rubber cement, magazines, construction paper and scissors.

_____ Eyeball the posterboard. Decide where to place the headline, details and pictures. Don't include too much or too little. Balance is the key.

_____ Vary the size of letters. Use graphic letters; trace letters; cut out letters from construction paper. Use markers, crayons or paint.

_____ Use rubber cement to secure magazine pictures or clip art.

_____ Double-check spelling. Make sure all pertinent information has been included.

_____ Hang the poster in a prominent place such as the youth room, church office, fellowship hall or some place in the community.

_____ Remember to take down the poster after the event!

Appreciation Letter

Send appreciation letters often. You can never say thanks too often!

Thank-you's are appropriate for adults who have fixed a snack for refreshments, helped with transportation, been guest speakers or resource people for programs, raised money for an event or provided scholarships, provided free materials or services to the youth group, chaperoned an activity, taught a youth class or sponsored the youth group, hosted a youth activity, or stood up as advocates for youth ministry in church committees or board meetings.

Send thank-you notes to young people for leading activities at an event or a meeting, doing outstanding jobs in the youth group, working hard at a fund raiser, rendering any special service or planning and implementing a youth activity.

Remember to thank church staff members for the work they do as well. Even though they may be paid for their work, thank-you notes are especially encouraging in their ministries.

Handwritten notes tend to express more care than copied form letters. Handwriting takes a little longer—which makes them more valuable.

APPRECIATION LETTER

(Sample)

Dear Tim,
   I want you to know how much the youth group and I appreciate the work you did at the last chili supper. Your service greatly supports our congregation's youth ministry.

   Too often we forget to say thank you for the many ways you have demonstrated your love and caring for the young people in our congregation. For all of your past support and your future assistance, we give thanks to God.

       Yours in ministry with youth,

         Larry
        Youth Minister

Scholarship Recommendation Letter

A s a youth minister, you will have the opportunity to write scholarship recommendations for some of your youth group members. It is flattering for a junior or senior to ask you to help out.

Since each scholarship is different, your approach to writing a recommendation letter will vary. In all letters, clearly state the nature of your relationship with the student and the general qualities that make the student unique. If the scholarship is based on certain criteria, use those requirements to formulate the section of qualities or skills you recognize in this individual.

Be sure to offer reasons or give examples for your comments. Avoid superlative adjectives such as "best," "fantastic," "marvelous" and so on. You want your young person to get the scholarship, but most review committees can see right through inflated recommendation letters.

Be professional in your approach. Use church letterhead (unless the scholarship uses a specific form). Write letters to meet a specific need. Know the scholarship's requirements and deadlines. Explain why you think this young person would be a good choice for receiving this award. Check your spelling, punctuation, grammar and typing. Well-written scholarship recommendation letters can be a real ministry to youth group members who need help paying for their education.

SCHOLARSHIP RECOMMENDATION LETTER

(Sample)

February 27, 1990

To Whom It May Concern:

It is my pleasure to recommend John Moore for the Union Tech Scholarship.

John and I met each other when I became youth leader at First Baptist Church in Westminster, California. During his high school years, John has participated in many activities with the church youth group. While watching John interact with a variety of people in a variety of situations, I've noticed the following personal characteristics that help John stand "above the crowd":

● John shows respect to those in positions of leadership and authority. He also demonstrates patience with those who operate below his own level of maturity.
● John pursues his own interests, even when they are not the common pastimes of his peers.
● John thinks for himself. He listens to others' opinions, then carefully sifts through all available information before making up his own mind.

Because of such qualities, John has been a joy to work with at church. I have also come to know him as a friend. I believe his stable personality and strong character will benefit any college he attends.

Granting John Moore the Union Tech Scholarship would help him begin his college experience on a positive note. This same decision would also be a positive reflection on Union Tech.

Sincerely,

Bonnie

Bonnie Harrold
Youth Minister

Calling Chain

The calling chain can be a valuable tool for informing group members of prayer needs or program changes. Fill in the names and numbers of your youth group members and supply everyone with a completed copy.

When you need to contact all group members, simply activate the chain at the top and let each person call the person or people underneath him or her in the chart. If someone cannot reach an individual in the middle of the chain, he or she should take responsibility to contact the person directly below that individual so the chain can continue. If it is necessary to alter the chain in this way, the individual who made the change is responsible for contacting the person he or she skipped over.

The people whose names are located at the end of the chain should contact the leader to let him or her know that the message has been received and that section of the chain is complete.

CALLING CHAIN

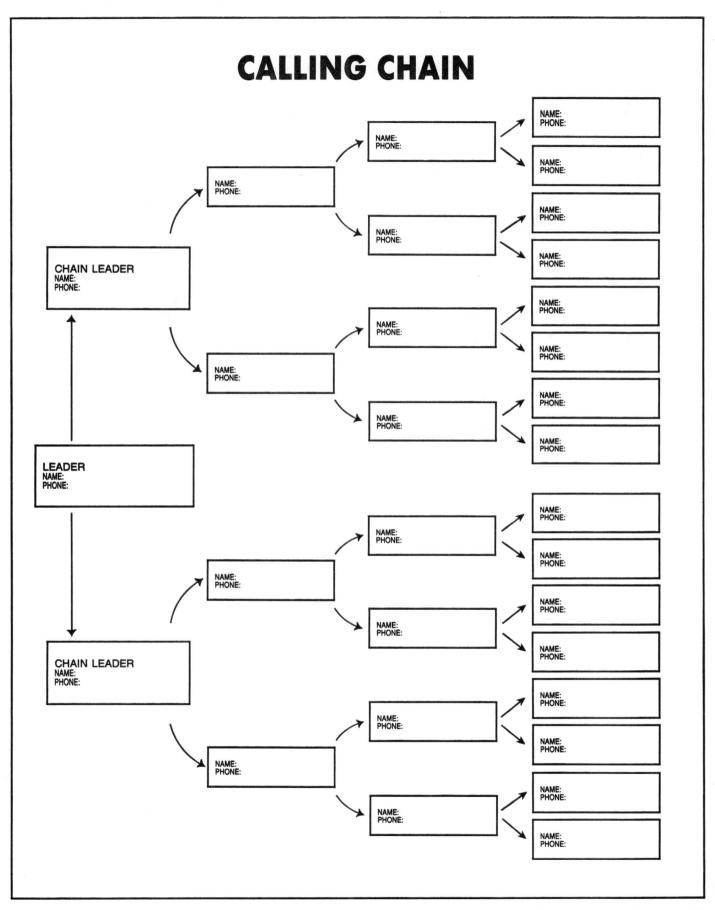

Sign-Up Sheets

What kind of response do you get when you announce that sign-up sheets are available in the back of the church? Do you end up with blank sheets or sheets with one or two names on them? Here are a few suggestions with samples of better ways to encourage people to sign up for whatever reason (to volunteer, attend a program, bring food, etc.).

The first characteristic of a usable sign-up sheet is its uniqueness. Don't just post a sheet of paper with lines numbered 1 to 25. It's unlikely to draw much attention. The three examples that follow will catch the attention of those who walk by. The Crowd Sign-Up has people sign up in one of the silhouettes on the form. The Sign-Up Wheel attaches a circle on top of the information sheet using a brass fastener. The Sign-Up Steps asks people to sign up on one of the steps.

Be creative. Draw your own sign-up sheet. Match the form to the event or need. For example, one group planned a picnic for the Fourth of July. They purchased a large watermelon and placed it in the back of the room. Then they asked those who would attend the picnic to sign their names on the watermelon with a marker.

Always provide a pencil, marker or crayon with the sign-up sheet. This makes it easy for individuals to add their names to the list. It's also helpful to solicit a few signatures before you put the form on the wall. No one likes to be first, but people are more than willing to add their names to lists that are already started.

GET INVOLVED!

SIGN UP

TODAY!

JOIN THE CROWD

SIGN YOUR NAME ON ONE OF THE PEOPLE!

SIGN-UP WHEEL

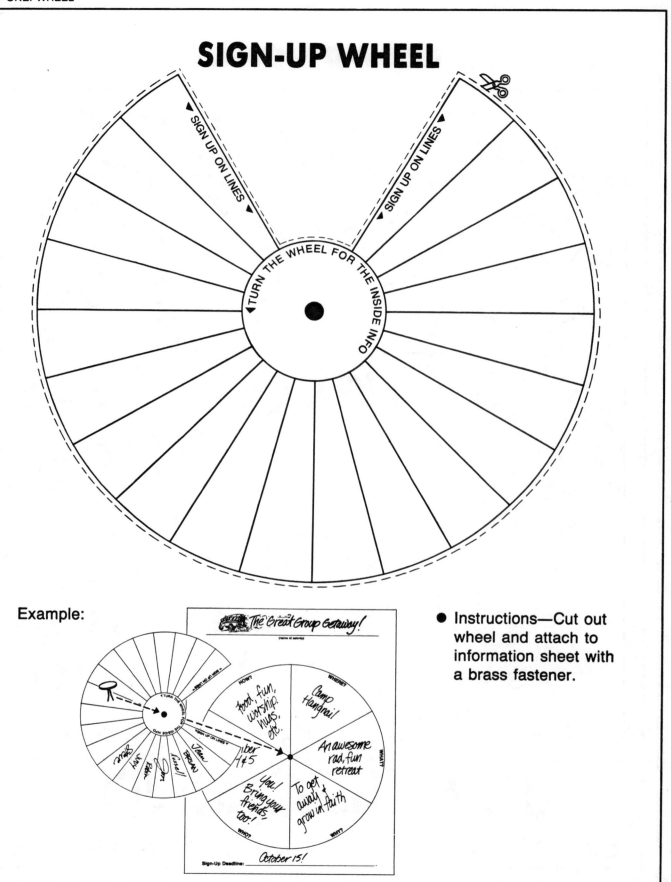

SIGN UP ON LINES ▶

SIGN UP ON LINES ▶

◀ TURN THE WHEEL FOR THE INSIDE INFO

Example:

● Instructions—Cut out wheel and attach to information sheet with a brass fastener.

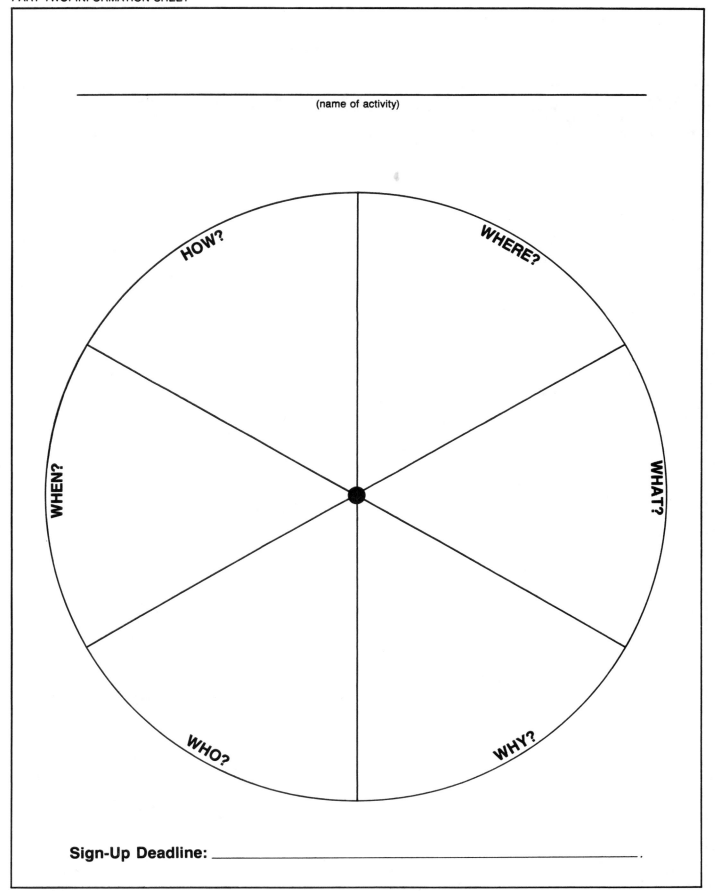

_____
(name of activity)

Sign-Up Deadline: _____.

ARE YOU COMING OR GOING?

EITHER WAY, SIGN UP TODAY!

WHAT:

WHEN

WHERE:

WHAT TO BRING:

Place your name on a step →

SIGN UP HERE

THINGS AREN'T ALWAYS AS THEY MIGHT APPEAR. BUT... WE WANT YOU TO APPEAR WITH US! PLEASE SIGN UP NOW!

SIGN-UP DEADLINE: _____

Awards and Personal Recognition

Teenagers need lots of affirmation. A good way to help build a group member's self-esteem is to award him or her special recognition. The following forms are examples of the many awards you might give your kids.

These examples include a No-Reason-Whatsoever Award (award this to someone who needs a boost); a generic Award of Excellence (mark the boxes that apply); and a Thanks for Being You! Award (an award of affirmation).

AWARDS AND PERSONAL RECOGNITION (A)

N.R.W. AWARD

(THE NO-REASON-WHATSOEVER AWARD)

Is presented to:

_____
(Name of recipient)

For no reason whatsoever.
Well, at least I didn't think of a reason at first,
But come to think of it
You just deserved some kind of award!

_____
(Name of church)
Youth Fellowship

Signed _____

This award is given to the recipient without his or her prior knowledge
And for no reason whatsoever.
Nevertheless, it is an award
And should make you feel proud to receive it.
Void where prohibited by law.

AWARDS AND PERSONAL RECOGNITION (B)

This

Award of Excellence

Is presented to: _____

(Choose at least one from each list)

FOR:
- ☐ Outstanding
- ☐ Incredible
- ☐ Stupendous
- ☐ Exceptional
- ☐ Extraordinary
- ☐ _____

- ☐ Creativity
- ☐ Courage
- ☐ Leadership
- ☐ Musical talent
- ☐ Athletic skill
- ☐ _____

As witnessed by the body of family and friends known as

_____ **Youth Fellowship**
(Name of church)

on _____ _____, _____
(Month)   (Day)   (Year)

Thanks!!!

Youth leader _____

AWARDS AND PERSONAL RECOGNITION (C)

Suggestion: Paste a picture of the recipient in the center of the seal.

THANKS FOR BEING YOU! AWARD

The _____ AWARD
(Name of recipient)

Is given to:

_____
(Name of recipient)

Just because you ARE:

_____
(Name of recipient)

Presented by

_____
(Name of church)
Youth Fellowship

Thanks for being you!

Signed: _____

Copyright Permission Letter

Need music for your next meeting? Better have permission from the copyright owner before you run it off. Want to use that article you just read for your next Bible study? Same thing. Better have permission before you make copies for the whole group.

Ten years ago you may not have needed this form. Today it's different. The availability of copy machines has changed everything. This may be the most useful form you'll find for your programming.

Seems like a pain, right? But asking for permission to reprint material isn't nearly as painful as legal prosecution, which has involved several churches already. Don't flirt with this possibility. Plan ahead. Secure permission from the copyright owner to use legally protected material.

COPYRIGHT PERMISSION LETTER

Address of church
City, state, Zip code
Date

Copyright source
Attn: Rights and Permissions
Street address
City, state, Zip code

Dear _____:

    I am _____ at _____. Some
              (Position)   (Church name)
of my responsibilities include _____

_____.

    I recently had the privilege of reading/hearing your _____

_____. I especially appreciated _____.

May we have permission to use _____
                       (Material you want to use)
for _____ on _____?
   (Type of use you have in mind)   (Date)

    We expect to make _____ copies. We do not intend to charge
                 (Number)
a fee for these copies.

    Let me know if there is additional information I can share with you
regarding this request. Please send us information regarding permission
status, credit line and any expected fee.

Sincerely yours,

_____
       (Name)

PART NINE:

Records

Weekly Expense Record

The Internal Revenue Service requires ministry professionals to keep a detailed and complete record of all business-related expenses. Save receipts when you purchase meals, books, lodging, etc. If you do not keep a record of mileage but record actual transportation expenses (such as gasoline, repairs and maintenance), record all costs and attach accompanying receipts.

Remember to consult the IRS regulations concerning all deductions related to business expenses. Seek the advice of a certified public accountant when you have questions.

WEEKLY EXPENSE RECORD

Week of _____
(Month, day, year)

Auto mileage and gas expense

Date	Mileage	Gas expenses	Destinations and ministry tasks	Receipts attached

Professional expenses (Meals, lodging, books, seminar fees, etc.)

Date	Cost	Description	Receipts

_____
Youth minister

Check/Refund Request

M ost youth ministry expenses can and should be budgeted. When you plan ahead, you can have the cash or a check prepared in advance.

But there are times when costs exceed what you plan. Or you need to pick up something on your way to work. A group member may forget to take the cash when she goes to pick up the film you have rented, or a volunteer may decide to save a trip to the store by purchasing the group's refreshments while doing his own shopping. All of these examples illustrate the types of group expenses that come out of someone's own pocket.

The following form offers a quick and easy way for people to get reimbursed. Attaching a receipt provides an excellent record of money you or someone else in the group has spent.

Copy page 153 and cut into four separate forms.

CHECK/REFUND REQUEST

Check/Refund Request

_____
(Name of church)

Date:_____ Amount: _____
Comments: _____
_____

Charge to:
☐ Education (seminars, workshops, classes)
☐ Audio-visual materials (films, tapes, rentals)
☐ Books, magazines, curriculum materials
☐ Worship   ☐ Trip   ☐ Refreshments
☐ Supplies   ☐ Retreat   ☐ Other: _____
☐ Car expense   ☐ _____

Make check payable to:
Name _____
Address _____
City_____State_____Zip_____
Approved by _____ Check no. _____
Attach receipt to this form

Check/Refund Request

_____
(Name of church)

Date:_____ Amount: _____
Comments: _____
_____

Charge to:
☐ Education (seminars, workshops, classes)
☐ Audio-visual materials (films, tapes, rentals)
☐ Books, magazines, curriculum materials
☐ Worship   ☐ Trip   ☐ Refreshments
☐ Supplies   ☐ Retreat   ☐ Other: _____
☐ Car expense   ☐ _____

Make check payable to:
Name _____
Address _____
City_____State_____Zip_____
Approved by _____ Check no. _____
Attach receipt to this form

Check/Refund Request

_____
(Name of church)

Date:_____ Amount: _____
Comments: _____
_____

Charge to:
☐ Education (seminars, workshops, classes)
☐ Audio-visual materials (films, tapes, rentals)
☐ Books, magazines, curriculum materials
☐ Worship   ☐ Trip   ☐ Refreshments
☐ Supplies   ☐ Retreat   ☐ Other: _____
☐ Car expense   ☐ _____

Make check payable to:
Name _____
Address _____
City_____State_____Zip_____
Approved by _____ Check no. _____
Attach receipt to this form

Check/Refund Request

_____
(Name of church)

Date:_____ Amount: _____
Comments: _____
_____

Charge to:
☐ Education (seminars, workshops, classes)
☐ Audio-visual materials (films, tapes, rentals)
☐ Books, magazines, curriculum materials
☐ Worship   ☐ Trip   ☐ Refreshments
☐ Supplies   ☐ Retreat   ☐ Other: _____
☐ Car expense   ☐ _____

Make check payable to:
Name _____
Address _____
City_____State_____Zip_____
Approved by _____ Check no. _____
Attach receipt to this form

Record of Long-Distance Calls

Recording your long-distance phone calls each month helps you keep track of whom you called, when you called and how much each call cost. You can review the list at the end of the month to decide if you are spending too much time or money on long-distance calls.

Keep your log next to the phone and develop the habit of recording each call as soon as you hang up. This is an expense log, so note only your long-distance calls. Put an "X" by any personal calls.

RECORD OF LONG-DISTANCE CALLS

_____

(Month)

Date	Time of day	Person or organization	Phone number	Total time	Charges
				Total:	$

Phone Call/Visitation Log

How do you keep track of your important conversations with youth group members, volunteers and others? Do you just commit the conversation to memory and hope for the best?

Here is a simple form you can use to record the main thrust of your phone calls or visits. Mark the appropriate box and fill out the form soon after the conversation. Refer to the completed forms weekly for evaluation and planning.

PHONE CALL/VISITATION LOG

Name: _____

☐ I called   ☐ He/she called
☐ I visited   ☐ He/she visited
Date of contact: Time:
Address:
Phone number:
Reason for contact:

Subject of conversation:
Excerpts from conversation:

Follow-up:
   Action to be taken:
   Call back on:
Comments:

Length of call/visit:

Youth Ministry Roster

A youth ministry roster gives you the following information at a glance:
- Correct spelling of your kids' names;
- Addresses;
- Phone numbers;
- Birth dates;
- Year in school;
- Names of schools; and
- Number of times and dates you have contacted the kids so far.

Always keep the membership roster up-to-date. Add new members' names when they join. Include all of the young people with whom the youth ministry has had contact. Have adult volunteers help you telephone each person each week. Membership rosters help you maintain personal contact with each youth group member.

YOUTH MINISTRY ROSTER

_____
(Year)

Name	Address	Phone	Birth date	Year in school	Name of school	In-home visit (Date)

Supplies Inventory

If you've ever had trouble remembering what supplies you had available for your youth ministry meetings, programs and events, this form is for you. Use this form in three ways:

First, use it to prepare a master inventory for all the youth ministry supplies you currently have on hand.

Second, as you plan for a specific event, use the master inventory and a blank copy of this same form to list supplies you will need from your existing stock. This prepared list will help you remember everything you might need and list items you want to purchase.

Third, after your event, check the remaining supplies, adjust your inventory and make a list to replenish your materials.

Many items are essential to one youth group but meaningless to another. Use the blank spaces to list items you have on hand that are important for your youth group. Remember to keep a file containing the current master inventory. Update it regularly so you aren't surprised as you plan for a major event.

SUPPLIES INVENTORY

This form can be used for three different purposes. Mark the appropriate box below to indicate the purpose intended.

☐ **A** Master inventory list   Date of inventory _____
(Current in-stock record)

☐ **B** Supplies needed list   Date needed _____
(Items needed for an event)   Title of event _____
     Coordinator _____

☐ **C** Items to purchase

Item Description	A Current stock	B Event needs	C Purchase needs
Scissors			
Staplers			
Staples			
Rulers			
Masking tape			
Cellophane tape			
Duct tape			
All-purpose glue			
Straight pins			
_____			
_____			
Markers			
Pens			
Pencils			
Crayons			
Newsprint (pads/rolls)			
Lined paper			
Note paper			
3×5 cards			
Construction paper			
_____			
_____			
_____			

(over)

Item Description	A Current stock	B Event needs	C Purchase needs
Newspapers			
Magazines			
Plastic trash bags			
Paper sacks			
Balloons			
String			
Cloth scraps			
Felt			
Name tags			
Songbooks/songsheets			
Bibles			
Easels			
Puppets			
Weather balloons			
Volleyballs			
Volleyball net			
Footballs			
Baseballs			
Bats			
Softballs			
Basketballs			
Soccer balls			
Flying discs			

Agenda/Minutes

Meetings in the church can be a big headache for young people and adults alike. But it doesn't have to be that way!

A simple remedy may be to prepare a well-planned agenda. Distribute it several days ahead of time. People like to know what decisions they will be asked to make. Since they've had several days to think about the agenda topics, the quality of decisions at the meeting will tend to be better than going into the meeting "cold."

Meeting goals may be anything from program evaluation to sharing feelings of affirmation for a job well-done. Minutes don't have to be wordy to be helpful. Brief statements should highlight past discussions and committee reports and indicate decisions to be made, especially *who* is to do *what* and *when* it should be done. Leave room for participants to insert their own notes.

AGENDA/MINUTES

(Sample)

Organization or committee: Youth council and support group

Location: Youth room

Presiding: Assoc. Pastor Paul

Who should attend:

Assoc. Pastor Paul

Graduation committee

Pastor Mumford

Exec. committee

Youth council

Date: April 27

Begin meeting: 7:00 p.m.

End meeting: 8:15 p.m.

Secretary: Annie K.

Agenda (Meeting goals)	**Minutes** (Discussion highlights/decisions made)
1. Affirmation--carwash	1. 85% attendance. Earned $187.67 after expenses
2. Retreat speaker	2. Suggestions: Ken Davis, Bill White, Rev. Mike Pauley Decision:
3. Graduation committee	3. Gifts for group--Bibles, "Dare Book" (on table in narthex) Decision:
4. Prom-A-Rama	4.
5. Fall retreat	5. Place: Cost: Theme:
6.	6.
7.	7.
8.	8.

If you need to add something to this agenda, contact Pastor Paul by noon, Wed. April 22.

AGENDA/MINUTES

Organization or committee: _____   Date: _____

_____   Begin meeting:_____

Location: _____   End meeting: _____

Presiding: _____   Secretary: _____

Who should attend: _____   _____

_____   _____   _____

_____   _____   _____

_____   _____   _____

_____   _____   _____

_____   _____   _____

Agenda
(Meeting goals)

1.

2.

3.

4.

5.

6.

7.

8.

Minutes
(Discussion highlights/decisions made)

1.

2.

3.

4.

5.

6.

7.

8.

If you need to add something to this agenda, contact _____
(Name)

by _____.
(Time, date)

Routing Slip

How many times have you read something you would like to share with others? You pass the material to one person and plan on getting it back to share with someone else. Meanwhile the person you passed it to has passed it on to someone else or misplaced it in his or her office. So you can't pass it and you can't use it again.

A routing slip is a form you attach to material you want others to read. On this form write a brief description of the material you are routing on the line below the heading. If it is a magazine, be sure to include the name and date. If it is a letter, be sure to indicate the author of the letter, the date and the number of pages you are sending. When you have several loose pages, you may want to staple them and place them in a folder, attaching the routing slip to the folder.

Check the box next to each person whom you want to see this material. In this way you will control where it will go. If there are special pages for certain individuals, write those page numbers next to their names. For example, if you want the choir director to read pages 4 through 7, write those numbers next to her name.

Remember to include a realistic date for when you need the material returned or when everyone needs to have seen the contents. This date and specific instructions on how long each person should keep the material will help individuals to keep the material moving. Be sure you indicate to whom the material needs to be returned, or if it needs to be trashed after everyone is through with it. A routing slip not only helps make sure everyone has seen the material, but it lets the reader know how much time he or she has to peruse the contents. It also helps others be responsible for returning this material to you.

ROUTING SLIP

(Sample)
"Keep Me on the Right Trail"

GROUP Magazine—May, 1987
<u>(Description, name, date)</u>

This material needs to make a brief stop with each of the people checked below. Help it stay on the right trail so it can end its trip on time. Please keep for no more than 1 day(s) and pass it on. Thanks for your help!

Date sent: April 5

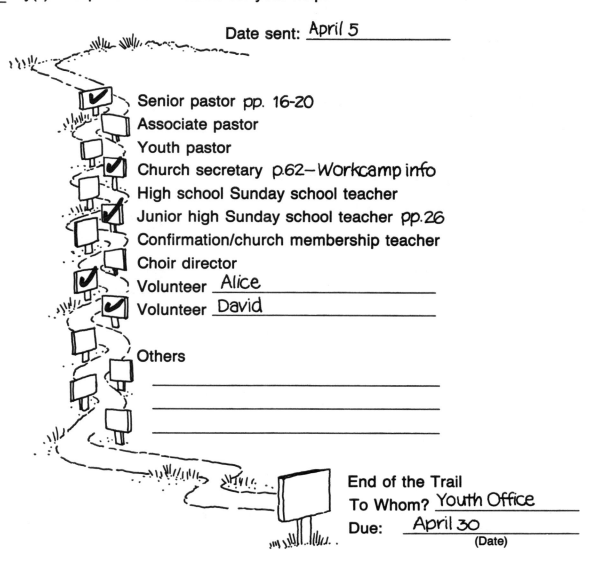

Senior pastor pp. 16-20

Associate pastor

Youth pastor

Church secretary p.62—Workcamp info

High school Sunday school teacher

Junior high Sunday school teacher pp.26

Confirmation/church membership teacher

Choir director

Volunteer Alice

Volunteer David

Others

_____

_____

_____

End of the Trail

To Whom? Youth Office

Due: April 30
(Date)

ROUTING SLIP

"Keep Me on the Right Trail"

_____
(Description, name, date)

This material needs to make a brief stop with each of the people checked below. Help it stay on the right trail so it can end its trip on time. Please keep for no more than ___ day(s) and pass it on. Thanks for your help!

Date sent: _____

Senior pastor
Associate pastor
Youth pastor
Church secretary
High school Sunday school teacher
Junior high Sunday school teacher
Confirmation/church membership teacher
Choir director
Volunteer _____
Volunteer _____
Others

_____
_____
_____

End of the Trail
To Whom? _____
Due: _____
(Date)

Preparing a Constitution

Constitutions often intimidate young people and adults alike. Yet all youth groups have a constitution even if it isn't written. In many cases their constitution is simply in the minds of those who are in charge.

In some instances we could say that our constitution is the "way we do things around here." Even if you anticipate unusual stability among your leaders, it's best to record rules and regulations for your group. It makes transitions much easier for new volunteers, pastors, youth leaders and the young people themselves.

A constitution is valuable because:

1. It provides a framework on which members of the group can organize and operate;

2. It spells out responsibilities, expectations and obligations of the group members to the group and to each other;

3. It helps all young people and adults focus on both the spiritual and organizational goals and purposes of the group; and

4. It provides consistency. Now everyone will know the correct procedures and what to do when.

Resist the temptation to use legalese. This kind of constitution does not need words like "herewith," "inasmuch," "hereinafter," etc.

This form makes it easy for each group to devise its own constitution, allowing for individual situations and circumstances.

PREPARING A CONSTITUTION

Article I—Name

The name of this youth group is the _____ of

_____.
(Church)

Article II—Affiliation

This youth group is affiliated with the national youth organization of

_____.
(Denomination)

Article III—Purposes

The purposes of this youth group are:

1.
2.
3.
4.
5.
6.
7.

Article IV—Membership

The following individuals are eligible for membership in this youth group:

1.
2.
3.

Article V—Steering committee (Young people)

The steering committee of this youth group will be determined by _____.
(Whom or what)

Their responsibilities for each _____ term of call will consist of:
(Length of time)

1.
2.
3.
4.

Article VI—Administration (Adults)

The adult administrative team of this youth group will be determined by

_____. Their responsibilities for each _____
(Whom or what)   (Length of time)

term of call will consist of:

1.
2.
3.
4.
5.
6.
7.
8.
9.

Fast Forms for Youth Ministry Contributors

Steve Parolini
Activity and Interest Inventory
Awards and Personal Recognition
Calling Chain
Fund-Raising Sponsor Sheet
Letter of Call for Volunteer Youth Worker
Newsletter Production Worksheet
Parent Letter for Activities
Parent Survey
Personal Information
Phone Call/Visitation Log
Planning a Fund Raiser
Planning an Event
Scholarship Recommendation Letter
Sign-Up Sheets
Sunday School Planning
Supplies Inventory
Travel Expense Log
Youth Council Job Descriptions
Youth Minister Resume

Larry Keefauver
Appreciation Letter
Conduct Covenants
Employee Evaluation
Letter of Call for Youth Minister
Meeting Evaluation
Meeting Planning Guide
Parent Information Form and Commitment Letter
Volunteer Youth Worker Job Description
Weekly Expense Record
Youth Minister Evaluations
Youth Minister Job Description

Cindy Hansen
Meeting Checklist
Poster Production Checklist
Retreat Checklists
Retreat Evaluation
Retreat Planning Checklist
Retreat Site Evaluation Checklist
Time Planners
Volunteer Evaluations
Youth Ministry Roster

Nancy Shaw
Check/Refund Request
Liability Release and Parental Consent Forms
Lodging Request
Menu/Shopping List
Routing Slip
Volunteer Profile
Volunteer Time, Talent and Interest Form
Whom to Contact

Dan Hansen
Agenda/Minutes
Copyright Permission Letter
Fund-Raising Accountability Form
Life Planning Inventory
Overnight Permission Letter
Preparation for Leading a Bible Study
Preparing a Constitution

Lee Sparks
Less-Stress Checklist
News Releases
Youth Ministry Calendar

Lane G. Eskew
Prayer List
Record of Long-Distance Calls

Thom and Joani Schultz
Youth Needs Surveys

INNOVATIVE RESOURCE IDEAS FOR YOUR MINISTRY...

Controversial Discussion Starters for Youth Ministry

Stephen Parolini

Now it's easy to lead your teenagers in finding Bible answers to today's tough issues like abortion, euthanasia, and New Age philosophy...plus, important practical-living issues, such as cheating in school and lying to parents. Each issue is presented with two opposing position statements and supporting Scriptures. Teenagers then form debate groups and have the opportunity to argue the right and wrong of each issue. As kids talk and check the Bible, they begin to form convictions that will stay with them for a lifetime.

ISBN 1-55945-156-4 $12.99

Devotions for Youth Groups On the Go

Dan and Cindy Hansen

Now it's easy to turn every youth group trip into an opportunity for spiritual growth for your kids. This first-of-its-kind resource gives you 52 easy-to-prepare devotions that teach meaningful spiritual lessons using the experiences of your group's favorite outings. You'll get devotions perfect for everything from amusement parks...to choir trips...to miniature golf...to the zoo. Your kids will gain new insights from the Bible as they...

- discuss how many "strikes" God gives us...after enjoying a game of softball,
- experience the hardship of Jesus' temptation in the wilderness...on a camping trip,
- understand the disciples' relief when Jesus calmed the storm...while white-water rafting, even

...learn to trust God's will when bad weather cancels an event or the bus breaks down!

Plus, the handy topical index and complete Scripture index make your planning easy.

ISBN 1-55945-075-4 $10.99

JAZZ UP YOUR PUBLICITY WITH CLIP ART FROM
Group®

Seasonal Clip-Art

Your church's publicity will stand out season after season with these ready-to-go designs. You'll make...

- professional-looking posters that attract crowds to your special programs,
- nifty newsletters that share your church's seasonal news,
- fabulous fliers to remind members of upcoming events,
- bright bulletins to showcase your worship services,

...and more! Plus, illustrations are varied in style and form to fit whatever design you're trying to match.

Seasonal Clip-Art is quick and easy to use. Find your season in the table of contents, pick the design and size you need, and photocopy for instant use! The creative results will attract attention and help build your ministry.

ISBN 1-55945-178-5 $15.99

Classy Clip Art

Illustrated by Dale Bargmann and Robert M. Moyer

Capture your kids' attention with more than 300 ready–to–use designs you'll use to add flair—and a touch of class—to your publicity. This one–of–a–kind collection of sophisticated designs has everything you'll need to produce...

- fabulous fliers,
- professional–looking posters,
- noteworthy newsletters,
- bold bulletins,
- handsome handouts, and
- colorful calendars.

You'll find just the art you need for all occasions, celebrations, programs, and events. Plus, each design comes in different sizes, so you can pick the one that fits best. Simply choose your art, paste it down, and duplicate it. The creative results will attract attention and help build your ministry!

ISBN 1-55945-020-7 $15.99

Outrageous Clip Art for Youth Ministry

Rand Kruback

Get hundreds of kooky clip art cartoons that teeter on the brink of bizarre. Delight your kids with easy-to-create, off-the-wall newsletters and announcements.

Plus, you'll get loads of unusual program ideas from this crazy clip art, including...
- burger bash,
- roller derby,
- lunch munch,
- pie party,
- water war,
- taco fiesta,
- bus brigade,
- frisbee fling,
- pancake feed.

And you'll grab kids' and parents' attention fast with not-so-typical ways to say...
- Oops!
- Be there!
- Happy Birthday!
- S-s-s-surprise!
- Thanks a lot
- Missed you
- Come and get it!
- Why me, Lord?

Add spark and spice to all your printed pieces. Boost attendance and excitement—with kid-pleasing art straight from the outer limits of Rand Kruback's bizarre imagination.

ISBN 0-931529-39-5 $15.99

Youth Ministry Clip Art

You'll get hundreds of pieces of ready-to-use artwork—in all kinds of sizes. Headlines. Cartoons. Borders. Everything you need to jazz up your printed pieces. Discover creative new ways to build enthusiasm for...

- special activities—trips, retreats, and holidays;
- meetings—dozens of topics including Bible studies, discipleship, peer pressure, and more;
- increasing attendance—calendars and reminders.

Using clip art is easy as 1-2-3! First, choose your art. Second, cut it out. Third, paste it on the page. Then, head to the nearest photocopier and turn out professional-looking and attention-grabbing newsletters, handouts, posters, fliers, and more! Plus, you'll find easy-to-follow directions, a fast index, and lots of suggestions to make your announcements shout!

ISBN 0-931529-26-3 $15.99